7/3/

ENGRAVED BY T. JOHNSON.

Walt Whitman
taken from life 1863
war time Washington
D C

WALT (Whitman)

The Good Gray Poet Speaks for Himself

BY
ELIZABETH CORBETT

Author of "Cecily and the Wide World,"
"The Vanished Helga" and "Puritan and Pagan"

FREDERICK A. STOKES COMPANY
NEW YORK : : : MCMXXVIII

To
GERTRUDE CORBETT PARK

CONTENTS

CONTENTS

CONTENTS

CONTENTS

"Allons! after the great companions! and to belong to them! They, too, are on the road!"

—"Song of the Open Road."

WALT

WALT

I

1826

LOUISA VAN VELSOR WHITMAN, WALT WHITMAN

In the well-scrubbed kitchen of a small house in Brooklyn, a capable young matron is enjoying an afternoon hour of leisure. That is, she is knitting industriously, rocking a cradle with her foot, and trying to keep up with the conversational demands of a seven-year-old boy.

"Run along and play with your brothers, Walt. 'Tis too fine a day for a great boy to be indoors."

"I played with them all the morning. Now I'd sooner stay here and talk with you."

"Then talk quietly, not to wake the baby."

"What shall we talk about quietly? I know! You tell me a story, Mother. Something that really happened, and something you never told me before."

"You have heard all the stories Mother knows."

"Then tell me about the big storm when we lived

[1]

down on Long Island. You know, while we lived in the house I was born in. I always like to hear that story."

"It isn't good for thee. It excites thee too much."

"That's why I like to hear it. Oh, I was excited that night! I thought the wind would blow our house down. I climbed down out of the loft and got in bed with you. Father put me back in my own bed, but I came down again."

"Thee did, Walt."

"Just as it was beginning to grow light a neighbor came to the door and shouted. There was a ship on the rocks just off our beach. Father ran to see if he could be of any help. He wouldn't take me with him. But you were busy with whoever was the baby then. So I slipped out when you weren't looking, and went down to the beach."

"That was disobedient. And it was no day for a very small boy to be out alone."

"I meant to find Father. I meant it as much as anything. But when I got down to the beach I forgot all about Father. The waves were coming in as tall as houses. And I could see the ship, only every one was calling it the wreck. The sailors tried to launch a boat, but it filled with water and sank. Then a woman came on the deck. I could tell it was a woman because her skirt blew. There was only one mast standing, but they tied her to that. The next day when the storm went down they found all the sailors drowned. But the woman was still tied to the mast, and she was frozen."

"I don't want thee to talk about it any more. All that next night thee kept crying in thy sleep and waking. Even now talking about it makes thy cheeks burn."

"But I like to talk about it, Mother. It makes me shake, but I like to shake that way."

"Jesse just ran past the door. Doesn't thee want to go and play with him?"

"Not when we're having such a good time telling stories. Thank you for telling me about the storm, Mother. Now it's my turn. This story is about a little boy who didn't stay back where the teacher told him to. And because he didn't do what he was told to he had great good luck."

"That same story, Walt?"

"Listen, Mother! When it's my turn, I tell which story I please. They were digging a great big hole in Brooklyn, because they were going to build a great big building. But before they built the building they had to lay the corner-stone. I don't know just why they had to, but they did. And just when they were going to lay the corner-stone, who should come to Brooklyn but Lafayette, the great general!"

"He had been a general, Walt. But he came this time as an old man, and in peace."

"The old soldiers were all out to see him. They stood with their hats off while he was driven past them. He was in a yellow coach, and it drove slowly, and the people all cheered. But he didn't pay much attention. He was looking ahead at the school children who were all around the big hole."

"Thee mustn't always think people are looking at thee."

"Maybe people don't, but Lafayette did. Listen, Mother! Lafayette got out of his yellow coach, and came up to the big hole. Some of the men started to put the littlest children into better places, so that they could see things and wouldn't fall. Lafayette helped them. And the first child he lifted and set down was little Walt Whitman. It was me, Mother! And he kissed me."

"It was a pleasant happening. But thee mustn't be a goose about it."

"Mother, you say 'thee' to me only when you mean to scold. But my grandfather and grandmother say it all the time."

"That is because they are Quakers, Walt."

"The Quakers must be pretty nice people, because my grandfather, Major Van Velsor, is the nicest man I know. I'd rather be with him in his apple orchard than any other place I know, except here with you. Why isn't my father a Quaker too?"

"Thy father is at heart as good a Quaker as any."

"But things bother him. Nothing bothers my grandfather."

"It isn't given to everybody to be contented."

"Elias Hicks isn't contented. He's the greatest Quaker of all, but he makes an awful lot of noise. Can't he preach loud!"

"Now, Walt!"

"I guess I know. I guess I remember the night I heard him. Father was fine to me that night. He came in with a load of kindling from a carpenter job, and he threw the sticks down and said, 'Mother, Elias Hicks preaches tonight. We are going to hear him. Walt may go along if he likes. He hasn't been bad lately, for him.' So I went along. I liked it very much."

"The spirit moved Elias powerfully that night."

"I know just how he felt. The spirit often moves

[4]

me. When I grow up I should like to be a preacher too."

"If thee succeeds in being as good a carpenter as thy father, that is all thee needs ask."

"But when I grow up I'm going to ask a lot."

"Thee won't get it, then."

"Maybe I will. Anyhow I won't be afraid to ask."

II

1830

EDWARD C. CLARKE, WALT WHITMAN

An elderly Brooklyn lawyer, who is also a sound scholar, has become interested in his errand-boy. He is a sturdy youngster of eleven, who carries a book under his arm most of the time. But when he strolls in late one summer afternoon he is devoting his attention to a fine large apple.

"Well, did you see Mr. Burr?"

"Saw him and gave him the message."

"Did you have trouble in getting across the river? You've been gone a long time."

"He kept me there talking to him."

"Did he, indeed? It's little enough he ever has to say to me, or to most people nowadays."

"Mr. Clarke, is that the Mr. Burr I've heard about? Burr who was a traitor and shot Hamilton?"

"I don't know whether he was a traitor. There might be two opinions about that. But he is Aaron Burr who shot Alexander Hamilton."

"That's queer to think of, Mr. Clarke. He's such a

neat little man, so old-fashioned and polite. And he talks to me as if I was grown up."

"What does he talk about, eh?"

"He asks me questions about the books I'm reading. I told him you subscribed to a library for me."

"I suppose he thinks I wasted my money. Indeed, he'd be right in a way. It's very little work I've had out of you since you've had all you want to read."

"He didn't say anything about wasting money. He asked if I'd read the Arabian Nights. Then he talked to me about a man named Marco Polo, who went to China before any one else went there, and came back with his clothes sewed full of jewels. I thought that sounded like more Arabian Nights, but Mr. Burr says it all happened."

"Ay, Walt. So the books have it."

"Oh, do you think I can get the book that tells about Marco Polo?"

"I think you can. If not this summer, then another summer. You've a long life ahead of you to read in."

"But I'd rather have the book this summer. I'd rather have it tomorrow."

"I dare say you would. You're a greedy reader. Did Burr talk to you about anything else?"

"Part of the time I didn't listen. I was thinking about Marco Polo coming back from China with jewels sewed in his clothes. But Mr. Burr was most polite to me. When I came away he gave me this apple. He always gives me some piece of fruit. If it isn't an apple it's a pear."

"St, st! throw the core in the wood-box, not on the floor. There are no more errands today. You can read until closing time, if you like."

"I always like that. H'm."

"H'm."

"Mr. Clarke!"

"I said read, Walt. I didn't say interrupt me when I'm working."

"Yes. But, Mr. Clarke, I just happened to think——"

"Well, well, out with it and get it over! What did you think?"

"If Mr. Burr talked out, instead of just being polite and old-fashioned—You know, if he didn't ask a boy questions, but told instead what had happened to him himself——"

"If Aaron Burr told what had happened to him?"

"Oh, I know he wouldn't! But if he did, I think he could beat Marco Polo. He could beat even the Arabian Nights."

III

1831

WILLIAM HARTSHORNE, WALT WHITMAN

*The basement of an old building on
Fulton Street, Brooklyn. Here William Hartshorne, a veteran printer,
sets the type of the Long Island
Star. The press and a small station-
ery-shop are on the street-floor.
Hartshorne is a great stickler on all
points connected with the craft. Also
he dearly loves an audience. A prom-
ising apprentice who likes to listen is
a great find.*

"You'd best stand on the type-box, boy. Or pile
up two or three old cases. The upper case is the length
of your arm away from you."

"But I have a long reach already, Mr. Hartshorne.
And I'm still growing. Now that I know where things
are, I can find them ever so fast."

"Let's see if you really know, or only think you
know. Lay down your stick and shut your eyes. Now
keep your eyes shut and show me where the *e* box is."

"That's easy. It's so big."

"Now the box for spaces."

"That's here, close to me."

[11]

"The *a* box. That's right. The *i* box. The *o* box. The box for quads."

"There! I didn't mean to open my eyes. But the box for quads is away in the right-hand corner, and my eyes came open when I reached."

"That's good enough, Walt."

"I guess it is pretty good, Mr. Hartshorne. When I first came here to set type I didn't know enough to put my thumb in the stick. And the first line of type I ever set I pressed too hard with my thumb, and burst it."

"All beginners do that. Now pick up your stick and go ahead with your work."

"Upper case *L, o, n, g.* Upper case *I, s, l, a, n, d.* Was there another newspaper in Brooklyn before the Star, Mr. Hartshorne?"

"Ay, lad, long before. There was the *Courier and Long Island Advertizer.* I was present at the first issue of the paper. Let me see, that would be in 1799."

"Was it printed in this building?"

"Get on with your work, Walt. No, not in this building."

"But this is an old building, isn't it?"

"Ay. This building was standing at the time of the Revolution."

"Are there many other such old buildings still standing?"

"Not many. And even those there are don't look the same. The Barnet Johnson house was standing then, but was approached by the creek much nearer than it is at present. I mind that, because that was where the boat used to row in to get water for the prison ships."

"What prison ships?"

"The British ships. It was where they kept American prisoners. They were anchored off Brooklyn. There were five or six of them, but I remember the *Old Jersey* best. The *Jersey* was the worst of them."

"You mean the British kept American prisoners on boats right here in the Bay?"

"That's exactly what I mean. The British held Brooklyn during most of the Revolution. Only they didn't keep the prisoners. Mostly they starved or bayoneted them."

"You mean the British were cruel to their prisoners?"

"Look 'ee, Walt, there was one boat came and went steady between the ships and the shore, fetching water from the spring up near where Kent Avenue is now. They didn't fetch half enough water at that. The prisoners were always thirsty, and a guard with a bayonet was stationed night and day at the water-cask. But there was another boat came every day from the ships to the shore, bringing to land the bodies of prisoners who had died on board."

"Did they bring the bodies to land to bury them?"

"If burying you could call it. They dug down a foot or so in the sand. Buried 'em just deep enough so the wind wouldn't blow the covering away."

"Then we boys, when we play down there on the beach, digging in the sand and kicking it about—we may kick up a prisoner's bones?"

"No need to squeeze the type if you did, Walt. There you've burst a line just like a beginner!"

"But I can't think of my thumb when I think of the bones of prisoners kicked about in the sand."

"You never found any to kick, did you? They were all disposed of long ago."

"Who picked them up?"

"A man named Benjamin Romaine. Leastways it was done on his account. He had been on the *Old Jersey* himself. He had a temple built over the bones, and left word in his will he was to be buried there too. A 'temple' was what he called it, though 'twas but a wooden shed at best, and its best was long ago."

"You don't mean that tumble-down shed on Hudson Avenue next the Navy Yard?"

"Ay, Walt. That's just what I mean."

"People don't care much about bones of their patriots, do they?"

"They think they care, Walt. But they forget. That shed was never meant to stand so long. A wonderful building was to take its place. But no one ever got around to build it. Put more marks in that sentence there. Parentheses aren't enough. Use commas too, both before and after."

"Comma, parenthesis—parenthesis, comma. Like that?"

"Ay. You're learning."

"Parenthesis, comma. But I don't think people should forget their dead patriots."

"They don't forget 'em exactly. Leastways they had a rare doings when they put the bones in the vault under the temple. And that was long after the Revolution."

"How long after?"

"It would be in 1808. April, 1808, they laid the corner-stone, and in May they deposited the bones."

"What sort of rare doings did they have?"

"When they laid the corner-stone it was like laying any other corner-stone."

"Then you don't have to tell me about that. I was there when Lafayette laid the corner-stone of the Apprentices' Library. I was only a child, but I remember it well. Lafayette took me up in his arms and lifted me to a better place to see. Then before he set me down he kissed me."

"I've heard you tell about it, Walt. More than once, in fact."

"But how about the day when they deposited the bones?"

"Ah, that was a day! It was fine spring weather, and a great procession formed about the middle of the forenoon in front of the City Hall over in New York."

"Did you see the procession?"

"Ay, boy. I wouldn't have missed it. Lengthy and imposing it was. Thousands of people in line, the Governor, the Mayor, the City Council, the Legislature. And then all the societies, the Freemasons, the Tammany Society, the Clergy, the Shipwrights, the Hibernians, the Tailors and Hatters and Coopers."

"I shouldn't think it such a treat to look at a lot of tailors marching. I'd rather see Lafayette."

"The societies that marched were the least of it. But perhaps you don't care to hear about the rest."

"Oh, tell me! Tell me, please. I'll try not to interrupt again."

"At the head of the whole procession was a trumpeter all dressed in black. He rode a black horse. From his trumpet hung a black banner with a motto, writ large so that every one could read it, 'Mortals,

[15]

avaunt! 11,500 spirits of the murdered brave, approach the tomb of honor, of glory, and of patriotism.' "

" 'The tomb of honor, of glory, and of patriotism,' That's splendid. Do go on."

"There was one section with thirteen coffins, representing the thirteen original States. These had as pall-bearers a hundred and four Revolutionary characters."

"Yes, that's eight to every coffin."

"In the next section was something even finer."

"What?"

"A great pedestal for a flagstaff, from which floated the American flag. On the front of the pedestal was the inscription, 'Americans, remember the British.' On the rear it said,

> " 'Tyrants dread the gathering storm,
> While freemen freemen's obsequies perform.' "

" 'While freemen freemen's obsequies perform.' That doesn't seem to swing along just right."

"It sounds all right to me. The whole thing was a brave sight. You'll scarcely meet with the like nowadays."

" 'While freemen freemen's—' It bothers me."

"What's that noise upstairs? It sounds as if Charley was shutting up shop."

"I guess he is."

"He's no business to do it until I give the order. Hello! It's much later than I thought."

"It got late early today. We've been so busy."

"You haven't learned much printing this afternoon, Walt. You've kept me yarning. But you can

set things to rights here while I go upstairs and find
out what the trouble is."

"Yes, sir. Quads on the right. 'While freemen
freemen's obsequies'— Oh, Mr. Hartshorne! Mr.
Hartshorne!"

"Hast stepped on a nail?"

"I just thought of something. It should be 'rite.' "

"Right or wrong, don't make such an outcry again."

"Right or left was what made me think of it. But
it's the other kind of rite. I mean in the line, you
know, instead of 'obsequies.' If you say, 'While freemen freemen's rites perform,' that makes it sound
better."

"It may. But that wasn't what the pedestal said."

"I guess I'm a better poet than the fellow who
wrote that line in the first place."

"Nothing to boast about if you were. An honest
printed page, well leaded, is worth all the trash the
poets rhyme."

"But doesn't even good printing go better on good
poetry?"

"Don't always be trying to have the last word,
Walt. Good printing is better than anything it can
possibly say."

IV

1832

SAMUEL CLEMENTS, WALT WHITMAN

Outside the office of the Long Island Patriot *in Brooklyn the junior printer lounges on a fine Sunday afternoon. The proprietor, Mr. Clements, usually takes him riding on Sunday. But today the patience of thirteen is pretty well worn through when at length the hook-nosed Clements comes driving up in his buggy.*

"Hello, Walt! Had you given me up?"

"I was just going home. I was tired of waiting."

"Hadn't you any work to put in time on?"

"Murphy left me with some work to finish. But I finished it long ago."

"I'm glad I caught you before you left. Jump in. That's the boy. Where did Murphy go?"

"He said he had to meet some one."

"I suppose he had. Murphy's already learning to be a politician. With his name it was to be expected. Well, if he had stayed we should have had to take him with us. Two's company. Which way shall we go?"

"I like to ride out in the country on Sunday afternoons."

"Better than you like to go to church on Sunday mornings, I dare say."

"I don't go to church except when you take me. My father is a Quaker, or almost a Quaker, but we don't go even to Quaker meetings."

"If your father is a Quaker, he may not like my taking you to the Dutch Reformed Church."

"I don't think he minds. He doesn't much mind what I do, so long as I keep out of his way."

"That's a good kind of father to have. Live and let live. Do you know that I've Quaker blood myself?"

"No, sir. I thought you were a Southerner."

"You thought I was a Southerner because I dared to defend slavery? Well, what if I am? These whey-faced abolitionists are only taking advantage of accident. In the North it never paid to keep slaves, because they had to be fed during the long cold winter. It was cheaper to hire white men, and when winter came turn them out to starve. Some stingy Yankee made that discovery, and his grandson is now the only righteous man on earth. Shouts for abolition, and damns you if you don't agree with him."

"The abolitionists do make a lot of noise. My father takes in their new paper. But I've heard my grandfather say his father kept slaves right on Long Island. You'd like my grandfather, old Major Van Velsor."

"Van Velsor, eh? That's a good Dutch name. 'Twould be only natural, boy, if you took to the Dutch church."

"But there's the Quaker business, Mr. Clements. Both my father and my mother were great admirers of Elias Hicks."

"Of—Elias—Hicks?"

"Elias Hicks the great Quaker preacher. Did you never hear of him? I've heard him preach."

"Did you like his preaching?"

"I liked to see the rows and rows of people listening. I liked the looks of Hicks himself. But his preaching was like most other preaching."

"I'm afraid you show a worldly mind."

"Couldn't a man preach to people, and tell them things that would be of some use to them?"

"Apparently not, Walt. At least they never do."

"Just the same, I liked the looks of Hicks. He's dead now, isn't he?"

"He died a year or so ago. Do you want to drive, now that we're out in the country?"

"I always like to drive."

"Go ahead, then. I'll lean back and smoke a cigar. I've had an exhausting Sunday, all on account of this same Elias Hicks. It's queer you should mention him today."

"But you just said Elias Hicks was dead. How could he tire you out when he's dead?"

"It's just because he's dead that he did tire me. Never mind looking at me, Walt. Watch your horse."

"But I was trying to think how he could tire you out when he's dead."

"I've a good mind to tell you. It isn't the sort of thing a man usually tells a boy. But then you aren't the usual sort of boy. And this is quite too good to keep."

"I'm not such a boy. I'm thirteen, and an experienced typesetter."

"You can hold your tongue, I·think. That's half the

battle of life, young man, holding your tongue. I'll maybe wish I'd held mine. But if you could have seen how funny Browen looked when he realized that his profits were gone! His profits, when it was my idea!"

"Who is Browen?"

"Calls himself a sculptor. One of these fellows who can pinch clay into shapes. It makes 'em think they have brains when the clay begins to look like something. Really they have only thumbs."

"Then this man Browen knows what you are going to tell me?"

"He will keep his mouth shut. For reasons, Walt, for reasons. Don't let the horse turn down that road. He's been that way once today. Once was enough."

"I have never seen Browen, have I?"

"You might see him if you took that very road we aren't taking. He is a few miles out that way, burying the last traces of his crime. Don't look so startled, Walt. I'm not a murderer. I'm more like a resurrectionist."

"I'm afraid I don't understand."

"You don't, but you will. Drive slowly. The horse is tired. To go back to Elias Hicks: The great Quaker preacher, after dividing the Quaker sect by the worst schism it has ever known, died about a year ago. We may suppose his soul went to Heaven, but his mortal part was buried at Jericho on Long Island."

"That road we didn't take is the road to Jericho."

"Well, this fellow Browen comes to me in his cups, and weeps because he's never made a bust of Hicks. He could have sold half a dozen busts to Hicks' followers if he'd had 'em to sell. But he hasn't so much as a clay model, and here's Hicks dead and buried."

"Wasn't there a picture of Hicks that he could go by?"

"There was one painting. Browen had been looking at it, and that was why he got drunk. 'It's flat, Clements,' says he between sobs. 'It's flat, and Hicks was so beautifully kn—kn—knobby.' "

"He was knobby. I remember that."

"I got to thinking what a shame it was that beautiful knobbiness should be wasted. Hicks had gone to the Quaker Heaven and we couldn't do him any harm. His mortal knobs were Browen's business. So Browen and I drove this very nag of mine out to Jericho on a dark night—but not too dark."

"You went out to where Hicks was buried?"

"For a little while we stopped being Quakers. Like good Prayer Book Christians, we believed in the resurrection of the body."

"You don't mean you—you dug him up!"

"We dug him up and made him immortal. Browen took two casts of his face and head. Two, d'ye see, in case of accident. Then we replanted Elias as neatly as the best of Quakers could have done it. If I hadn't the Long Island *Patriot* on my hands, I should have made a very good sexton."

"Weren't you afraid people would guess when they saw the busts?"

"No, I wasn't. Browen was. He said anybody ought to know the busts were made from a cast. I think he lay awake nights and trembled at the idea of being mobbed by indignant Quakers. Just the same, he went ahead and finished the busts. Three of them."

"D' you suppose I could get a look at them, Mr.

Clements? I'd like to see them, though I suppose they would make me shiver."

"I appreciate your curiosity, Walt. Don't ever let anybody tell you curiosity is a vice. For any man worthy of the name, it stands right at the head of the virtues. But I don't know how you'll manage to see the busts, unless you become a resurrectionist yourself."

"You didn't bury the busts too?"

"I simply buried the pieces. I buried them in order to avoid awkward explanations."

"You buried the pieces? What do you mean?"

"I mean that Browen was a young fool. The whole thing was my idea, in the first place. It was my daring that carried the idea through. It was my money that bought the marble for the busts. But this fool Browen, because he knew how to take a cast and make a mold from it, must assume that the profits would all be his. And, d'ye see, there weren't any profits to quarrel about. He had made three busts, but he hadn't sold any."

"But he quarreled with you?"

"Quarreled with himself. Took an axe and broke the busts. Broke the molds too, and faced me afterward as if he had done something heroic. I'd a good mind to take the axe to him. Instead I buried the pieces, out the Jericho road, but not so far out as Jericho. It serves me right, in a way, for getting mixed up with one of these artists."

"He—he broke the busts!"

"Here, give me the reins. You can't drive even a tired nag if you're going to blubber like a baby."

"But the busts weren't his to break."

"I had paid for the marble. But I'll charge that up to experience."

"The busts weren't yours either. They belonged to themselves."

"That's a queer thing to say, Walt. But I see you're a good deal upset. I shouldn't have told you if I'd thought you would take it so to heart."

"I'm glad you told me. I like to know things. But I'm sorry for all the nice knobby busts that all the Quakers might have looked at and remembered their old preacher."

"Yes. And the busts wouldn't have spoiled it by preaching at 'em. We'll turn back now."

"Breaking the busts made it all wrong. But making them was making something."

"While I think of it, Walt, I want you to address the paper to the subscribers this week. Think you can write the names clearly?"

"I'll take pains with them."

"You haven't done that part of the job before, have you?"

"No. But I like to do them all in turn."

"That's good. That's curiosity, if it isn't enterprise."

"I want to find out all about running a paper. I hope to have a paper of my own some day."

"I've no doubt you will, if you can stick to your trade and not go getting mixed up with these artist numskulls. You don't work as hard as Murphy, but I like the look of you better. That is, in general I like the look of you. But there was a moment just now when you looked for all the world like that young fool Browen."

V

1839

JAMES BRENTON, MRS. BRENTON

*The ground-floor bedroom in the
house of James Brenton, editor and
proprietor of the Long Island Democrat, at Jamaica. After his midday
dinner Brenton has come in here and
thrown himself on the bed. But he
has not eluded Mrs. Brenton, a woman who neither rests nor allows
rest in her neighborhood.*

"I want to talk to you for a few minutes, Jim."

"Can't you wait till after supper? I thought I'd
like a little nap."

"I don't know why I should wait. Besides, there's
too many people around after supper."

"You can send the boys to bed."

"Even if I did, there's that long-legged helper of
yours. At least he's called a helper."

"You needn't mind Walt, even if he should happen
to be around then. He sits and thinks, or reads to
himself. He never hears a word that's spoken."

"I guess I know he never hears a word. Night after
night he plants himself with a book right in front of

[27]

the dining-room closet, and stretches out his legs so
that I can't get past him to reach a thing."

"He wants a good light on his book. Tell him to
take his legs out of your way."

"I do tell him."

"Well, he takes 'em, don't he?"

"Yes, he does, without ever looking up from his
book. But the next time I want to get anything from
the closet there they are again blocking the passage."

"Well, tell him again to take his legs away."

"Maybe you think I never get tired of telling people
things."

"I know it makes extra work for you, having another person in the house. But I must have help with
the paper, and he has to stay somewhere."

"It isn't as if he was a mite of good with our own
boys. I thought when we took a printer who was the
school-teacher too he'd be good with our boys, sort
of tell 'em things and educate 'em a little. But he treats
'em 's if they was poison."

"They bother him when he wants to read."

"He's no call to be mean to 'em though."

"He's never what I'd call mean to 'em. Never
teases 'em, just asks 'em to not bother him."

"I'd like to know what more you want, Jim."

"All the boys at the school liked him, they say. He
never whipped any of them. He don't believe in whip-
ping. But when he said a thing they knew he meant it.
They liked to hear him talk, too. He talked to them
about all sorts of things."

"Too bad his school didn't last all the year. Since
the term ended he ha'n't done a thing but lay flat on

his back in the apple orchard and stare up at the blossoms till he went to sleep."

"Oh, the apple blossoms will soon be over!"

"When they are it'll just be something else. No good to talk to you, though; he's such a pet of yours."

"He's not a pet of mine. Sometimes I'm at my wits' end to make him work. He seems to think one time is just as good as another. But when I do get him started he's fine help. He learned the printing trade in Brooklyn, and learned it well. He can write, too. He ran a paper of his own over at Huntington two years ago."

"And let it go to smash, I'll be bound."

"It didn't smash. It's running yet. The *Long Islander*. He wrote the paper, printed it, delivered the copies himself with his own horse. You see he knows the business all through."

"If he had a good paper, why didn't he stick to it?"

"I asked him that once."

"What 'd he say?"

"Said he liked the place and the life and especially the long rides through the country, and stopping at all the farmhouses to talk when he delivered the paper. But he thought 'twas time he was moving on."

"Don't sound likely. I guess his paper was sold up."

"I don't know, I'm sure."

"Well, I've got to take your word for it, Jim. You always think you know. But I don't see how Walt could run a paper by sitting with his feet in everybody's way and coming to the table in his shirt-sleeves."

"It's always a clean shirt, anyway. And he sponges himself all over every day. That way he might set an example to our boys."

"Sponges himself every day, does he? I'm sure a

person can be clean enough without going to such lengths."

"I never had a helper before who bothered you by being too clean."

"You won't listen to a word against Walt. I know that."

"Haven't I just listened to several?"

"I had hopes last week that he might quit. One day he was talking to a neighbor outside—he didn't know the window was open. He said he'd thought about getting another school for the fall term."

"That's just what I've been afraid of."

"Well, you needn't be. He won't quit."

"He will some time."

"But I spoke to him about it just now."

"You didn't! What did he say?"

"Just smiled in that lazy way of his and said he didn't know as he'd make any change. He said he was pretty well satisfied here."

"I hope he didn't think I had anything to do with your speaking to him. I'd like to keep him. But I suppose for his own sake he ought not to settle down in a country town on Long Island. A bright young fellow like Walt could do something that amounts to something."

"If Walt ever does anything that amounts to something—"

"Yes, my dear? That's right. Close the door behind you when you go out. I'd still like that nap if I can get it. You were saying—?"

"I was saying, if Walt Whitman ever amounts to anything, it will be because he stands still so long that something catches up to him from behind. That's all."

VI

1842

NED WILKINS, WALT WHITMAN

The reading-room of Tammany Hall, New York. Like most public reading-rooms, it furnishes a warm place for a quiet doze. In contrast to the prevailing idleness, at a table in a corner Walt Whitman is writing away for dear life, with a sizable pile of manuscript at his elbow. Ned Wilkins, a young dandy with silky black whiskers and an appallingly high white stock, loafs in. A practised disdain is his refuge from chronic ill health. But when he sees Walt his eye lights with mischief.

"How is the great work progressing, Walt?"

"Don't interrupt me again, Ned. Don't, there's a good fellow."

"Interrupt you? Heaven forbid! I merely wish to view the spectacle of your industry. And of course to admire its fruit. How goes 'Franklin Evans, or The Inebriate'?"

"You ought to know. You spent all yesterday afternoon reading it."

"It's wonderful what you can do on paper, Walt. In two days you've had three women in love with you."

"In love with Franklin Evans, not with me."

"The artist identifies himself with his creation. I repeat, three women in love with you, the virtuous wife, the flirtatious widow, and the murderous quadroon. Not to speak of the women whose child you pulled out of the mill-race by a floating ribbon. Don't imagine the mother's sentiment toward you was pure gratitude. You're an uncommonly attractive fellow."

"There must be a love story, Ned. The novel is to run a hundred printed pages. The hero has to do something besides drink."

"I don't see why. A really sincere drinker never has to do anything else. If Franklin Evans lived up to the reputation you give him, he wouldn't have time even for the vicious Margaret, let alone the virtuous Mary. Yet I dare say you're right at that. A drunkard's grave would be the only safe refuge for a man all the women run after."

"Franklin Evans doesn't fill a drunkard's grave."

"How are you going to keep him out of it? He has already signed one pledge, and it doesn't seem to do a particle of good."

"He—he signs another."

"Ha, ha! Runs the whole gamut of misery, don't he? And does the second vaccination take?"

"Don't mock my necessities, Ned. Parke Godwin has promised me seventy-five dollars in cash on the delivery of the manuscript."

"Then you're striking a blow for Walt Whitman rather than for the cause of temperance. Oh, listen to the song!

> " 'Stay, mortal, stay! nor heedless thus
>   Thy sure destruction seal:
> Within that cup there lurks a curse
>   Which all who drink shall feel.
> Disease and death, forever nigh,
>   Stand ready at the door;
> And eager wait to hear the cry,
>   Of, 'Give me one glass more!' ' "

"Never mind singing, Ned. And please don't get those sheets out of order."

"I say, though, here's a good passage right after 'Give me one glass more.' I mean Franklin Evans' experience with landladies. Came from the heart, that did. The overbearing landlady, and the slovenly, and the miserly. You've got the whole tribe down pat."

"Just the same, I'm working right now for the benefit of a landlady."

"Which one?"

"My present one."

"The sad experience continues?"

"Continues, and grows sadder if anything."

"There's only one way to be quit of the tribe, Walt. Get married."

"Get married on Parke Godwin's seventy-five dollars?"

"Seventy-five dollars isn't bad payment for three days' work, old man."

"I can't always keep going at this rate."

"Perhaps not. But you can always get work if you set properly about it."

"Do you call that an inviting prospect, Ned? Get a job of writing to order, and do it. Get another job, and do it. Sounds very dull to me."

[33]

"But getting jobs of one kind and another is a thing you're good at. How many different jobs have you held, up to the present? I don't mean commissions for novels. I mean jobs that would have been steady— if they had been."

"I never stopped to count."

"Are you sure you can count that high?"

"I began young. There was Clement's printing-office and Hartshorne's and Spooner's. But before that I was in Lawyer Clarke's office as errand-boy."

"That's four."

"After my family moved back to the country I taught school for a few years. Counting the school I taught in Norwich, and the one west of Babylon the following winter, and at Long Swamp in the spring, and Smithtown the following winter, and Woodbury two years ago—"

"That's nine. Where are all these places?"

"On Long Island."

"I didn't know it was so long as all that. Go on."

"I may have forgotten one or two. But in '39 I not only taught school at Jamaica but worked for Mr. Brenton on the Long Island *Democrat*. Before that I had edited the *Long Islander* myself, over at Huntington where the Whitmans come from. Did I ever tell you about that, Ned?"

"You mean you edited a country newspaper?"

"Not only edited, but wrote it. Not only wrote it, but printed it. Not only printed it, but delivered it myself, jogging about the country lanes and byways behind my good horse Nina. That was a pleasant way to become familiar with the country, to get in touch with common country people. You, Ned, who are urban, polished, sophisticated, you have no idea of the strength, sanity, rooted plainness and goodness, of the common American man and woman."

"What became of your paper?"

"It goes on, and I dare say will go on. I tired of it, and left. Leaving the paper wasn't so bad, but I did hate to sell Nina."

"You couldn't afford to bury yourself on a country paper, even if it did allow you to keep a horse. I suppose having been an editor helped you when you came back to New York?"

"It landed me as editor of the *Tattler*. But I wasn't sole editor, wasn't my own boss. I couldn't stick it."

"How about the Aurora? Weren't you on that too?"

"I had more room on the *Aurora*. But the paper itself was a scandal."

"I agree with you there. But if you're always going to be so particular, you must be out of a job oftener than you're in one."

"I can always go back to my trade."

"What trade?"

"The printer's."

"Aren't you spoiled for that?"

"Not in the least. I went back to it for a season when I returned to New York. I worked in the office of the *New World* as a printer. A printer perhaps is what I am at bottom. I care more for the clean white paper, the types and the ink, the solid but spacious look of a well-printed column, than I do for trash like 'Franklin Evans.'"

"Don't fool yourself, old fellow. You have the itch

for writing, same as the rest of us. It suits the way-
ward streak in you. You find a steady job irksome;
you've proved that. But writing is touch and go, touch
again and go again."

"Go again? On another 'Franklin Evans'? Never!
I've learned a lesson that's worth more to me than
Parke Godwin's seventy-five dollars."

"Never another 'Franklin Evans.' That's just the
beauty of writing. After 'Franklin Evans, or the
Inebriate,' try 'Evangeline Evans, or The Prostitute.'
Then 'Gwendolyn Evans, or The Virtuous Wife and
Mother,' in order to let virtue have its turn. But to
keep virtue from getting monotonous, let the next
number of the family be 'Edward Evans, or The
Country Newspaper Hack.' "

"At this rate I shan't even finish Franklin, to say
nothing of giving him younger brothers and sisters."

"I gather you'd be just as well pleased if I
moved on?"

"You're too good an audience, Ned. I'd rather talk
to you than send Franklin Evans along the road to
the second stricter pledge."

"I'll go if I must. Things seem rather slack today,
though. Or perhaps it's I that am slack. Sure I can't
be of any help to you if I stay? I'll promise to dry up."

"Dryness is what bothers me. If you really want
to help, run around the corner to the Pewter Mug.
Fetch a couple of gin cocktails."

"A couple or three? One for you and one for me
and one for Franklin Evans?"

"If you want one yourself, Ned, make it three. I've
got to get this thing finished."

VII

1845

EDGAR ALLAN POE, WALT WHITMAN

The office of the Broadway Journal, on the second story of a building in Duane Street, New York. The editor, a man with a beautiful delicate face, subdued and a little jaded, sits looking out of the window but not seeing what he looks at. A fresh-colored, free-striding young man, swinging a stick and wearing a flower in his buttonhole, opens the door.

"I'm looking for the editor, Mr. Edgar Poe."

"For the editor, did you say? Oh, yes! I'm Mr. Poe."

"My name is Walt Whitman. I'm not sure whether that means anything to you."

"If it doesn't, perhaps you can jog my memory. Sit down, Mr. Whitman. What can I do for you?"

"You had a piece of mine in your paper lately. 'Art Singing and Heart Singing,' it was called."

"I remember it. It was a good piece. You made your point very neatly."

"I'm gratified if you think so, Mr. Poe."

[37]

"I suppose you've come about the matter of payment?"

"Not that altogether. I wanted to see you and talk to you because I'm interested in your writing. I write myself, or try to."

"Or intend to, perhaps? A great many young men come to talk to me about the things they intend to write."

"Ah, but I've had a lot of pieces published! The *Democratic Review* has used several of my stories. There was 'Wild Frank's Return,' and 'Dumb Kate,' and 'The Angel of Tears.' And I've published a short novel called 'Franklin Evans.' That sold almost twenty thousand copies."

"I envy you, Mr. Whitman. I have never written anything which sold so well."

"The thing was more or less of a lark. I was offered cash payment, and wrote the novel in the reading-room of Tammany Hall, on a diet of gin cocktails. That made it all the better, you see, because 'Franklin Evans' was supposed to be a temperance novel."

"Such a transaction appeals to you as a lark? It may be a lark at first. Most things are. But later on the life of a literary hack grows intolerable. Be wise in time."

"That's just what I wanted to talk to you about. Suppose a man doesn't care just about getting into print or making money? Suppose he truly has it in him to say something?"

"He is simply unfortunate. No man can write anything that will make up for the lack of ordinary comforts and decencies for his loved ones."

"Not even 'Helen'?

   " 'Helen, thy beauty is to me
     Like those Nicæan barks of yore—' "

"Don't, please!"

   " '—barks of yore,
  That gently, o'er a perfumed sea
  The weary way-worn wanderer bore
  To his own native shore.'

That sounds like something worth while, doesn't it?"

"It sounds like something indeed, when you repeat it in that great voice of yours. You are very strong, and very young. You don't look, either, as if things would upset you. Perhaps you might weather through."

"If you think that, Mr. Poe—"

"I say you might. Yet the life is worse than you can have any idea of. There's the grinding poverty to begin with."

"But if I don't mind poverty?"

"If you don't mind poverty you're no poet. Don't let any overfed burgess persuade you to the contrary. With his abnormally keen senses a poet hates poverty worse than any one else hates it. Yet poverty isn't the worst you would have to face. Seeing other men go ahead of you isn't the worst. The worst is seeing your work, into which you have poured your very life-blood, deliberately misunderstood, twisted about, made the shuttlecock of the would-be wits. It is when that happens that you want to lie down and die."

"But you haven't, Mr. Poe! You haven't lain down and died. You've kept your temper and done your work. And you've cleared up a lot of things for the rest of us. Take for example that essay of yours about whether a poem should be long or short. I always liked 'em short myself; but I thought perhaps that was my natural laziness. When I'd read what you had to say I felt the matter was settled once and for all. All poems should be short."

"Is it poetry that you want to write? You were speaking of stories."

"I've tried poetry too. But this that I speak of, I don't quite see as a poem. Yet I don't know what else it could be. I'd like to write a piece about the seashore."

"A piece about the seashore?"

"That makes you smile. But you see I've spent so much of my life on the seashore. As a child we lived out on Long Island. I go to the shore now, Sundays and other times. Often I am alone there for a whole day."

"That may show only that you like to be alone."

"Sometimes I wake in the night. Then I see and hear always the same thing, see and hear it quite plainly."

"And what is that?"

"A stretch of interminable white-brown sand, with the ocean perpetually and grandly rolling in upon it. And the sound is a rustle and a hiss, and a constant thump, thump, thump of low bass drums."

" 'Interminable sand, with the ocean perpetually rolling in upon it.' You may never write that poem, Mr. Whitman. But if you keep that vision with you, you will write no more trash, not even trash that sells twenty thousand copies."

"You see what I want, even if you think I'm a fool

for wanting it. Was that a clock striking? It must be noon. What a brute I've been to take up so much of a busy man's time!"

"I can make up the time tonight, if necessary. I often work late. Come in again, Mr. Whitman. But what a grip of iron! Have a little mercy on less sinewy persons."

"I gripped harder than I intended. I'm grateful to you, so grateful, not only for listening but for understanding."

"I was young once myself, though I was never young in the sense that you are. Shall we say I was not so sinewy?"

"Say what you please, so long as you smile at me like that. I'm going out while you are still smiling."

"Just a minute, Mr. Whitman! We were forgetting the little matter you came about. I regret having to offer you such a small sum. But the *Broadway Journal* is a poor paper."

"You can't insult me by offering me two dollars. I haven't had such a royal road as all that."

"You won't ever have a royal road. You won't listen to warnings. But for a man who scorns wisdom when it is offered, the next best thing is to be strong enough to get along without wisdom."

VIII

1848

HENRY MURPHY, ISAAC VAN ANDEN

*Since the days when he preferred pol-
itics to driving with Samuel Clements,
Henry Murphy has become a full-
fledged Irish politician. He is also the
backer of the Brooklyn* Daily Eagle.
In the office of the Eagle *he sits discussing the editor with the ostensible
proprietor, Isaac Van Anden.*

"You can see the figures for yourself, Mr. Murphy.
Whitman has been editor for two years. All during
those two years the circulation of the *Eagle* has fallen
off. It's been slow, but it's been steady. You can see
for yourself."

"I've seen the figures, Van Anden. They aren't con-
clusive. Up one month and down another. That's the
fortune of war. Or politics. Or newspapers."

"But I tell you we are losing money already. If
this goes on we shall lose more and more."

"Nonsense, Van Anden. That's the same as saying
that the people of Brooklyn don't appreciate a good
newspaper. You've been looking at your figures until
you squint. I've been looking at the paper itself."

"Oh, the paper ain't so bad! But Whitman thinks
you can run a city daily same as you could a country

[43]

weekly. He's never too busy to knock off for a swim in the middle of the day."

"He might do worse. Some editors knock off for a drink."

"Even when he's here, he don't work half the time. Yesterday I came in here when they weren't looking for me, and found the whole staff not working. They were gathered around Whitman, and he was reading out loud a new book of Carlyle's that had come in to be reviewed. The fellows we are paying good money to, sat with their mouths open like young robins."

"But, damn it all, Van Anden, new books are news! The *Eagle* gives more space to book reviews than any other paper in Brooklyn, or for that matter in New York. People have learned to watch for Whitman's reviews."

"Reviews seem to be his main idea. He does all the concert and theater reviews himself."

"And does them well, don't he?"

"Does 'em well enough. Going to the theater is the kind of hard work he likes. But when one of the theaters sends him a puff, he won't run it. Says that ain't honest."

"You mean run as if it was his own opinion a puff written by the theater manager? Well, I agree with him. That isn't honest."

"All the other papers do it. Besides, he's pretty radical on slavery."

"The *Eagle* is supposed to be a free-soil paper. So far as I know, he's not an abolitionist."

"Well, look here. Here's a clipping that was lying on his desk. He evidently means to make an editorial of it."

"It's clipped from the Natchez, Mississippi, *Free Trader* of February eleventh."

"Go on, Mr. Murphy. Read it."

"It seems to be an advertisement, signed by one Asa L. Thomson, and dated at Forks Road, Natchez, on February second. It reads, 'I have just arrived from Missouri with ten Negroes, which I will sell at a bargain. I have several boys about 21 years of age that are very likely, strictly No. 1. One fine seamstress and house servant, very likely. Those who wish to purchase and will buy the lot I will most certainly give a great bargain.' H'm—m—m—m."

"He could make quite an editorial out of that, couldn't he?"

"He is pretty fond of his opinions."

"I know you like Whitman, Mr. Murphy. I like him myself, so far as that goes. But I don't let my liking stand in my way."

"I've known him a long time, Van Anden. We were boys together on the old Long Island *Patriot*. I had to laugh last week when some one came running to me with a story that Whitman had kicked a friend of yours downstairs. I can't imagine good easy-going Walt kicking anybody downstairs."

"He didn't. Robinson was in such a hurry to get out of Whitman's way that he fell downstairs."

"Who'd you say it was?"

"Billy Robinson."

"Billy Robinson? But Robinson's a good party man, and a hard worker. What business had Whitman getting in a row with him?"

"Billy was just pointing out that there is a difference between before and after elections."

"But don't the fool know there is?"

"No, he don't. Robinson couldn't make him see it any more than I can."

"Why didn't Robinson himself come to me with this story?"

"He'd been warned it wouldn't do him any good. Whitman is such a favorite of yours."

"Favorite, hell! Every paper has a policy, Van Anden. We ain't in Heaven yet."

"You're beginning to see the point, Mr. Murphy. It's a choice between keeping Whitman and keeping the *Eagle*."

"You don't think he might quit of his own account?"

"He's never said anything about quitting."

"He's been with us two years, and two years is a long time for him to stay in one place."

"He's settling down, Mr. Murphy. He moved about a lot before he came to us. But he has a good berth on the *Eagle,* and he knows it."

"He must be thirty years old by this time. I suppose his Dutch blood is beginning to tell. He used to say he had Dutch blood."

"Good Dutch blood, Mr. Murphy. I hate to discharge him. But I want to keep my paper."

"I want to keep my constituents. In fact, I've got to keep them."

"Perhaps you'd discharge him yourself, Mr. Murphy? He'd take it better from you."

"You'll discharge him if you want it done, Van Anden. But you'd better have a couple of the other fellows handy when you do it. Whitman didn't kick Billy Robinson downstairs. But perhaps that was because it didn't occur to him."

IX

1848

EDWARD McCLURE, WALT WHITMAN

In the lobby of the old Broadway Theater, New York, a bell has just sounded to call loungers back to their seats for the next act. An impulsive gentleman from the South collides at the door with a casual but powerful person who is moving in the same direction.

"Damn you, Sir! Can't you look where you are going?"

"That is just my trouble. I was looking where I was going."

"Were you, indeed? I shouldn't have guessed it."

"I was looking where I was going. But I should have been looking to see who else was going in the same direction."

"Ha! That's a new view of it."

"I trust I haven't hurt you? I did come down on your foot."

"You did. The foot will never be quite the same again. How much do you weigh anyhow?"

"A little over two hundred. Hasn't our collision made you faint?"

[47]

"Why should it make me faint, sir?"

"Because if it had, I thought we might go in next door for a drink. I owe you that much apology."

"A drink is never out of order. But if we have it now, we shall miss part of the next act."

"If we miss part of an act, we can come back tomorrow night and see it."

"Free with your money, aren't you?"

"I came in on a pass."

"Not a newspaper pass, is it?"

"In a manner of speaking, it is."

"That's interesting. I think I shall accept your kind offer. A drink it is."

"Right this way. The beer in here is very good. People are beginning to drink beer instead of ale. But perhaps you would prefer something stronger?"

"I should. Beer is all right for you young fellows. To me it is simply slop. I'll take brandy. Now tell me what paper you work for."

"Not for any just now."

"Mean to say you're out of a job?"

"I've been out since this morning. Before this morning I was editor of the Brooklyn *Daily Eagle*."

"You quit the *Eagle* this morning?"

"I didn't quit. I was fired. A little matter of politics."

"Fired on account of your politics? Well, those things happen. I suppose you're looking for another job more in sympathy with your opinions?"

"There's no hurry. The theaters will all pass me in, and a good supply of oysters is cheap at any of the stalls. I wanted to see Booth tonight when I wouldn't have to think of writing him up. Junius Brutus Booth is a very great actor. Don't you think so?"

"You sound as if you had planned to loaf. I've never loafed much myself. I'm a busy man. I own a newspaper."

"Do you, indeed? The last newspaper owner I talked with I put out of his office. But I'm afraid I was hasty with him."

"That was this morning? One is enough for one day, isn't it? Come, isn't it?"

"Isn't what? I'm afraid I wasn't listening. I heard the audience clap just then. Booth must have come on the stage."

"Forget Booth for the present. We can see Booth even in New Orleans."

"In New Orleans, did you say? You don't sound like a Southerner."

"How do you know how Southerners sound? Ever been South?"

"No, but I've always wanted to go. New Orleans is an interesting place, by all I hear of it."

"It's the one place in America that is more interesting than anything you can possibly hear about it. I'm starting a new paper there, in opposition to the old *Picayune*. I call my paper the *Crescent*. I came North for presses and capital. But if I found a good man or two, I could use them too."

"There are plenty of good newspaper men in New York. They are easier to find than good presses."

"What should you say to giving a Southern job a trial?"

"Me?"

[49]

"You said you were out of work, didn't you?"

"I was calculating to loaf for a spell. Besides New Orleans is a long way to walk."

"That needn't bother you. I can advance you money. No need to lift an eyebrow at me. It isn't the brandy talking; it's McClure. See here, I think I have enough money with me now. Let me make sure. Fifty, one hundred—two hundred and ten dollars. I'll keep the ten dollars for cab fare. The two hundred will take you to New Orleans and a bit over for lagnappe."

"You mean I'm to take this money as an advance, and go to New Orleans to work on your paper?"

"If you take the money, that binds the bargain. That's right, pick it up. Try to get to New Orleans by the first of March, will you? We want to begin publishing as soon as possible."

"I'll get there in March, anyhow. I think I shall enjoy spring in the South."

"That's right. I like a man who doesn't shilly-shally. I see we are going to get on famously."

"Shan't we go in now and see Booth?"

"We might as well, though it will be rather a come-down. When you reach my age you will find that the lobby of a theater is often more amusing than the stage."

"I'll let you go ahead this time, Mr. McClure. You will feel safer. Hear them clap! Booth must be very good tonight. I've heard they have French opera in New Orleans."

"We have. Very good French opera."

"I suppose you're sitting in a box, Mr. McClure?"

"As it happens, I am."

"Then we separate here. I'm down with the groundlings. I shall see you again in March, at the office of the New Orleans *Crescent*. That's right, isn't it?"

"Just a minute, my casual friend! I've no doubt our appointment will be kept. But just as a matter of business—"

"Yes, Mr. McClure?"

"I'd like to know your name."

7 / 3 /

X

1848

FERNANDE DESMOULINS, WALT WHITMAN

A May night in an old New Orleans garden. Tropical flowers, a full moon, a stone bench under the shade of bougainvillea. A wooden door in the solid wall has been left ajar for somebody's secret entrance. Through it presently comes a dark young beauty ripe for love. She wears a light cloak, and carries a black silk mask. After a glance around she calls softly for her companion. He also carries a mask, and is in evening dress. He has a sense of high adventure, but it is the girl who takes the lead throughout. She speaks in a rich, husky voice, without a trace of accent. But sometimes she hesitates as if she were mentally translating from another tongue.

"Shut the door. It latches inside."
"I have latched it."

[53]

"Now come over here and sit down. Even a stone bench is a seat, after all those hours of dancing."

"What a very beautiful garden! Is it yours?"

"Yes. At least, it belongs to my father."

"To your father?"

"Why should that surprise you? Oh, I see! Most of the ladies whom you have escorted home from masked balls have no visible fathers."

"Most girls who have wealthy fathers do not go to masked balls."

"They do not if the fathers know about it. But what would you have? Doubtless in his day my father was young too. But as a father he is just like all the rest."

"This must be an old garden."

"Spread my cloak to keep off the dew. And strip off your gloves. We are no longer dancing."

"There are flowers here that I have never even seen elsewhere."

"It is a fine garden, and old too, as things go in America."

"You have not always lived in America?"

"I have not lived here since I was a little girl. The French of New Orleans send their daughters abroad to be educated."

"And when they are educated, they bring them back to New Orleans?"

"Of course. Bring them back to be married."

"You are not—married?"

"But no. The prospect does not attract me."

"I suppose you have many suitors?"

"Suitors enough. Too many. But these New Orleans young men take a wife as they would buy a new gun,

or a new nigger. There is no hurry. A woman is young
but the once."

"But in Paris, weren't you in a convent?"

"Paris was better, even in a convent. Besides, a convent— You do not know much about convents?"

"Nothing."

"In a convent, there was at lease the fun of tricking
the nuns. They were good women, you understand,
but nuns."

"You mean you tricked them by smuggling in books?
We talked so much about poetry while we were dancing."

"Books were smuggled in, yes. But notes were smuggled out. Glances crossed even in church. Perhaps a
cavalier waited all night in the shadow opposite the
convent wall. He never got in, you understand. But
it was pleasant to think of him waiting."

"Those young men you spoke of—your suitors—
does no one of them ever wait in the street here? Wait
all night perhaps, and wonder which is your window?"

"Wait in the street and get their feet tired? Not
they! Papa brings them to the house, and Fernande
meets them at dinner. Monsieur Such-a-one, Monsieur
This-other-thing. It is understood they are candidates
for her hand. Fernande is an only child, not a bad
match. They look her over."

"And then?"

"After dinner they sit and drink wine with Papa,
and make their proposals to him. Fernande is free to
stroll in the garden by herself, or to yawn over one
of those romances that she smuggled back from France.
So another day is gone. And presently her mulatto
maid will part the bed-curtains with her morning café."

"New Orleans is a city for men."

"You have found it so?"

"I have fallen in love with it."

"Tell me what in New Orleans you love."

"I have seen nothing in the North like its acre-large barrooms, and the pulsing life of its streets and squares. I think New Orleans sums itself up in the levees and the old French market. You, being a woman, have never loafed for hours on the crowded and bustling levees, making acquaintance among captains and boatmen, watching the gay lazy life of the wharf negroes, spontaneous as an animal's life, bursting of itself into dance and song. You have never spent a morning in the varied spectacle and curious scents of the old French market, tasting the admirable coffee, the cool 'cobblers,' the exquisite wines and perfect brandies."

"You call that a man's life?"

"Well, isn't it?"

"I call it simply an outsider's life, a Northerner's life. The real life of New Orleans takes place in lofty rooms darkened against the sun. The real life of New Orleans is the woman's life, the French woman's."

"Yet you were just saying the French woman had no life worth living here in New Orleans."

"Not at all. I was saying her life begins only with her love."

"Oh, love!"

"When I speak of love and women, I do not mean the quadroon girl who sells you flowers in the dusk. Take that flower out of your buttonhole. It is withered. I do not mean the women you have met at masked balls, who would love you for hire, and because you are handsome. I mean the woman who will love you for love's sake, and because it is in her blood to love."

"There are such women?"

"Perhaps. If you were lucky enough to meet one, you should know it without being told."

"If I met her at a masked ball, and danced through long hours with her, if I followed her home, and sat at her side in a garden that was already freshening toward the dawn——"

"If you did all that?"

"Even if I did, nothing could come of it for me, who am an outsider and a Northerner."

"Anything could come of it. Anything can. Anything at all, if you were the woman's lover."

"Fernande, don't look at me like that!"

"Shut your eyes, and you will not see how I look at you."

"My God, Fernande, you kiss like fire. Yet it's like moonlight too. And like falling water."

"And this? Is it like brandy or cool 'cobblers,' or even better?"

"Don't, don't! That is, just for a minute."

"Is it sweeter than brandy, and more stinging?"

"It is sweeter than Heaven. It is—too sweet."

"Lie back a moment with your head in the curve of my arm. I can kiss quietly too. On the forehead, so."

"Fernande, it is daybreak now."

"Is it? I'm not looking."

"If I came another night and stood in the shadow opposite this very gate— If I stood wondering which is your window——"

"I might send my mulatto maid down to let you in. Do not mistake her for me in the shadows. She looks very like me."

"You would send her down?"

"Perhaps I should come myself. For the ceiling of my room is very high, and dawn comes slowly behind the drawn blinds. Dawn will not come there for another hour, even tonight."

"I must give you time, Fernande. Tonight you are half mad, as I am. But another night, if you still mean it, I will come back."

"You mean to go now? Very well. Get up and go."

"There, I'm going. Let me kiss you once more. I'm going now."

"You've as good as gone. Why don't you finish?"

"I can't unlatch the gate."

"Pshaw! It has caught. Don't stop to worry with it. You might be discovered. Come through the house."

"But is this safe, to go through here?"

"It is very quiet, isn't it? Dark and quiet. Only the two of us afoot in this sleeping household. Give me your hand, and don't stumble. I know the way without a light."

"But this stairway, Fernande?"

"Turns here, and at the landing is an outside door. There. You see the street ahead of you. You smell the free air of a man's city."

"You know your power. Be satisfied. Another night."

"Another night, perhaps. Why don't you go? The door is open."

XI

1848

JEFF WHITMAN, WALT WHITMAN

A bedroom in the Fremont Hotel, New Orleans. Jeff, the fifteen-year old brother who has accompanied Walt on his southern journey, lies fast asleep behind the white mosquito-bars. In the first gray of dawn the door opens to admit Walt, who rushes over to the bed and shakes the sleeping boy.

"Wake up, Jeff. Wake up!"

"I say, Walt, it can't be breakfast time yet?"

"Sit up, Jeff, and get your eyes open. I want to tell you something."

"Oh, are you just getting in? You keep awfully queer hours lately. You haven't come in early one night this week."

"That's all over, Jeff. I know I've neglected you, brought you so far and then left you too much alone. But it's all over now. We're going back home."

"Home to Brooklyn? But when?"

"Today. There's a boat goes upriver at ten this morning. We go with it, if we have to sleep on deck."

"I'll be glad to go. I've been homesick right along, every day and every night. But I thought you liked it here."

"I liked it. Oh, yes, I liked it! But it's time I was moving on."

"You always want to move on, Walt. The brothers say that about you, Jesse and George and Andrew. George said you wouldn't stay in New Orleans three months. But we've stayed only two."

"Only two months. Is that all? Then it's not too much to wipe out of a man's mind and life. Two months that are as if they had never been."

"Shall I help you with the packing, Walt? Or are you going to have a little sleep?"

"I don't want any sleep. But you go to sleep again if you care to. There's time enough."

"If there's time enough to go back to sleep, why did you wake me?"

"Just to tell you that we're going. I thought it might be good news to you."

"It's good news enough, to think of getting back to Mother and all the boys. Ho, hum! I like living in a hotel, though, and picking just what I want to eat. Look here, Walt, you dropped something on the bed. Why, it's a picture! A picture of a lady."

"Here, give it to me!"

"I was going to give it to you. What makes you act so queer?"

"I didn't mean to snap at you, boy. Forgive me, won't you? I am queer. It's high time we left New Orleans."

"You can always come back another time if the

fancy strikes you. George says you can always get a job if you want it, he don't know why."

"I shall never come back here, Jeff. Never, never back to New Orleans."

"I guess you're right at that, Walt. Everything looks so nice, and the sunshine is so bright. But you have a feeling that underneath it's not nice at all."

"The city smiles at you, and then it stings."

"I know one thing I don't like, Walt. That's the slaves. Perhaps it's because we're Northerners—"

"Northerners and outsiders. So I've been told."

"—but I can't get used to slavery."

"I hope you never will get used to it. There are many kinds of slavery, and a man should never put up with any of them."

"Many kinds of slavery? What do you mean by that?"

"It's just some more of my queerness. Don't bother your head. Go to sleep, boy. I'll be better when you wake up."

XII

1849

FERNANDE DESMOULINS, WALT WHITMAN

Fernande, a shade more voluptuous and languid than she was a year ago, sits in her carefully shaded drawing-room with an open book in her lap. A mulatto servant admits a caller and withdraws. Seeing only that the caller is a man, Fernande lolls more gracefully. But when she sees what man it is her glance begins to sparkle with triumph, which later in the scene gives place to a kind of hunger.

"So you've come back!"

"Yes, Fernande, I've come back."

"Sit down and let me look at you. That's right. You look older than you did, but even handsomer. You've grown a little thin, and it's very becoming."

"I've grown a good deal thinner."

"Wasn't she as kind as she might have been?"

"She? Who?"

"The woman you left me for."

"I didn't leave you for any woman. You know that."

"I've never understood why you did leave me. But

[63]

that's all ancient history. Won't you sit a little closer, so that I needn't scream? That is close enough! There are always likely to be people coming in."

"People coming in while I'm here?"

"But of course. Do you take my drawing-room for a wilderness?"

"I'm not much used to drawing-rooms."

"At least not to mine? You still blush charmingly, Walt. Had you a pleasant journey from the North?"

"Not the same as last year. That was in spring, and I took my time. This is autumn, and I was in a hurry to arrive. I stopped one day at Blennerhasset, because I used to be interested in Aaron Burr. But even there I couldn't keep my mind on what I saw."

"You in a hurry? I can't imagine it."

"Don't ridicule me, Fernande. I've been absent more than a year—"

"Is it so long as that?"

"You know it is. Long enough to learn many things."

"You sound as if they were rather dull things. If they are, don't talk about them. Tell me instead what you have been doing. Do you still read as much poetry as you used to?"

"I have written a few poems myself."

"But how interesting! Repeat them to me."

"Not now. They are unimportant. And when I tried to write about anything, other things kept getting mixed up with it."

"What sort of things?"

"Love things. Woman things."

"But that is important! What makes you say it isn't?"

"Listen, Fernande. This is important. I have been editing a paper. A paper of my own, in Brooklyn."

"What is its name?"

"The *Freeman*."

"Ah! A paper against slavery?"

"In a way, yes."

"Did you put my slaves into it? The mulatto maid who looks like me would make a good paragraph. She is just seven months younger than I am."

"The free-soil character of my paper isn't the point, Fernande. The point is that I have been working as I never worked in my life. I have made myself a position in the newspaper world, a position humble but secure."

"You must be a changed man."

"I had no thought of change when I first went North. I wanted to be the man I had been. If I had any idea beyond just that, it was to write a book some day."

"You plan to write a book? Indeed, you interest me."

"The day when I shall write that book is very distant, Fernande."

"Then while we are waiting for it, repeat some of your poems."

"I tell you you wouldn't like them."

"Perhaps not, but I am curious. Especially when you hint that it is love has turned you poet."

"I wanted to write about heroism and high endeavor, and how anything that has ever counted for good must continue to count."

"Yes?"

"But love kept getting in the way."

"Yes, Walt. It does. It gets abominably in the way."

"However, I didn't come here to scold you."

"That reminds me. Don't come in again as you came just now. I can trust my own maid, the one who looks like Papa. I mean like me. But the rest of the house servants are just common niggers. And Papa doesn't like Northerners."

"I came this way on purpose, Fernande, through the front door and ushered by your darky. Our being lovers last year was all right, if that had been all."

"How do you mean, if that had been all?"

"I left you last year without even bidding you good-by."

"You did. You need not remind me."

"I put the length and breadth of the country between us. I put in a year's work that would ordinarily have done me for five years. I put in my poems, damn them. I have forgotten other women in a week. After a year, I could only come back to you."

"I wouldn't like your gray hair on another man. But I like it on you. It makes you look sweet."

"You aren't listening to me."

"I'm looking at you. That is better."

"Fernande, I don't believe in love that lasts forever. I can't believe in anything until I see, feel, experience it. But this love between you and me has lasted."

"You believe that now?"

"It has lasted. Because it has, we must make a place for it in our lives."

"You were the sweetest lover I've had. I have not forgotten, Walt."

"I realize that you can't step down from your place here in New Orleans, and live in the scorn of your old

[66]

acquaintances. But there is a place for you now in the North, a place I have made for you. As yet it is not a high place. But I can improve it, must improve it, when I have you as help and stimulation."

"What are you talking about, my darling? You go on and on, but I don't seem to follow."

"I have come South this time to marry you."

"But I never said I should marry you, Walt. I never even thought of it."

"I have thought of it. It is the only course open to us. I must go to your father now, make him see what I see so clearly, settle the thing once and for all. Surely you, too, see that I must. You may put me off for a moment. But surely you see it as I do."

"Listen, Walt. This won't do. You have talked too long already. The afternoon is growing late, and even the club won't hold Papa much longer."

"I am ready for him whenever he comes. The sooner he comes, the better."

"You mustn't let him walk in on you here with me."

"But why not?"

"There would be trouble, terrible trouble, Papa wanting to shoot you, perhaps, and Fernande packed off to a convent."

"You think if I waited a day or two you could sound him out, prepare him?"

"I prepare him? Yes, of course. That is, I might be able to—prepare him. Come to me to-night, when we are sure of being alone, and we will talk further."

"If I come to you to-night, I come as your husband."

"Yes, yes. We can settle that later. Only go now."

"If I come back to-night, am I to wait outside the door in the garden wall?"

"No. Wait across the street, and around the corner. Don't pay attention to anything you see. Only wait. I will not keep you waiting longer than is necessary."

"You make my head swim, Fernande, when you come close to me like this."

"You still find it a little dizzying? It is so to me as well."

"But, remember, this time it is for life. As wife and husband, Fernande. As wife and husband."

"You could not forget Fernande, and Fernande has not forgotten. Before midnight, Walt, it may not be safe. But after midnight, oh, come quickly!"

XIII

1850

RAOUL DESMOULINS, WALT WHITMAN

> *A harassed Southern gentleman is*
> *spending a needed hour alone with a*
> *long stiff drink. The new year is be-*
> *ginning badly. But an impetuous*
> *young giant who has thrust past all*
> *the barricades of civilization shuts*
> *the door for himself, from the inside.*

"Damn that darky! I gave orders I wasn't to be dis-
turbed."

"It isn't his fault. I had to see you."

"I haven't the slightest desire to see you, sir. As
you found your own way in, perhaps you can find the
way out. If you can't I shall ring. I have more than one
darky in the house."

"You'd better not drag any one else in here just now.
You don't want a scene before your niggers. Where is
Fernande?"

"My daughter's whereabouts is my own affair. I fail
to see how it can interest you."

"Do you know where she is?"

"Of course I know."

"Is she here?"

"I'm not discussing that with you, sir. My daughter is well, and in safety. She is also fully occupied. If you have an idea of seeing her, dismiss it. You won't see her."

"She's well? She's here? Oh, thank God for that at least! Thank God!"

"I can forgive your agitation, Mr.———, ah, Mr.——— But it wearies me. If you came for reassurance about Fernande, you have it. I need not detain you longer."

"She is here in the house?"

"No, she isn't."

"Then you know where she is?"

"I have told you that I do."

"But perhaps you do not know where she has been?"

"Perhaps I do not wish to know. Perhaps it is just as well to let bygones be bygones. But as I judge from your speech that you are a Northerner, I take it upon myself to remind you that there are some things never mentioned in connection with a lady."

"Thank you for cooling me down. I shouldn't have rushed in like this. But I was sick with anxiety about Fernande."

"Indeed, Mr. ———?"

"My name is Whitman. Walt Whitman."

"I do not remember having heard the name."

"Did Fernande never mention it? But she told me——"

"I gather that you have been an admirer of my daughter's. Even a convent training will make a Desmoulins nothing but a Desmoulins. I have been a most careful father. But doubtless there are in any girl's life some episodes that are dark to even the most careful of fathers."

"I don't quite like the way you say that. But perhaps it's my fault that you speak as you do. I should have talked to you months ago. But Fernande held me off. May I sit down?"

"I have no wish to keep you standing. But I see no object in prolonging the interview."

"Perhaps Fernande could not tell you. Perhaps no girl could. But you must listen to me."

"I suppose if I listen I shall at least get it over. Go on."

"Mr. Desmoulins, I am a Northerner, as you have guessed. I came down here almost two years ago, to work on the *Crescent* newspaper."

"A silly sheet, run by Northerners who don't know what they are talking about. But go on."

"Soon after I came here I met your daughter."

"You met Fernande? I can't imagine where."

"At a masked ball. A public ball."

"At a public masked ball? The little bitch!"

"I fell in love with her at sight, and she with me."

"Doubtless she did. She went to the ball to find some one to fall in love with. But do I gather that you continued to meet her?"

"We met every night for a week."

"Evidently I haven't appreciated Fernande. Where did you meet her?"

"Here, in this house. She managed so that not even her maid knew of those meetings, I think."

"I'll have the nigger whipped to make sure. But go on."

"At first I treated the affair lightly enough. A girl fresh from a convent, with her head full of poetry and George Sand—spring and the scents of an old garden—

moonlight nights—a strange lover. I thought that was all."

"I agree with you. It undoubtedly was all."

"It was not. I went away for a year. When I came back last autumn, I appreciated for the first time the depth of my feeling and the earnestness of hers. I knew then that there was no course open to us except to live our lives together."

"You flattered yourself."

"A girl brought up as Fernande had been, surrounded as she was surrounded, couldn't walk out of the door and marry a penniless scribbler here in New Orleans. But back in my own country I make a livelihood. I asked her to marry me and go North with me."

"What had Fernande to say to that idea? She must have found it amusing."

"I couldn't get her to say anything. She wouldn't face the idea. She wouldn't let me come and see you. She wouldn't think or talk of anything but love."

"A headlong chit, isn't she? A great deal what I was at her age. If she had been a man Fernande would have used her youth to some purpose."

"We were both headlong. But Fernande talked love while I talked marriage."

"It isn't usually that way around, Mr. Whitman."

"At last I prevailed on her to leave with me for the North. I wished to be married before we left New Orleans. But Fernande argued for delay until we reached St. Louis. We had to wait over a boat there anyhow. Against my better judgment I agreed to St. Louis."

"So she went with you on the steamer to St. Louis? I think I can continue the story from there."

"Has Fernande told you?"

"I can conjecture. I have lived a long time in a world which, as you must have lately guessed, is not made for lovers. Besides, I know Fernande."

"Then you conjecture—?"

"My high-spirited daughter had seen you only by moonlight in a garden, or under other circumstances still more deceptive. She had thought of you only as a lover. Now she saw you in the chill of daily companionship, and in contrast to other men. You must have struck her as—well, uncouth."

"Hadn't I always struck her as uncouth? And hadn't she loved me for my uncouthness? But that day in St. Louis I was cruel to her. She had sickened on the journey up the river. She shuddered at the accommodations of our cheap hotel. That last morning—shall I ever forget that last morning!"

"That last morning you quarreled?"

"No, not quarreled. She cried because she had no maid, and couldn't manage her own hair. I tried to help her, and tangled it farther. It sounds like a trivial thing. But she turned on me in a fury, and ordered me out of the room. I went. It was only to make arrangements for our marriage. But I left her in tears."

"And then?"

"When I came back she was gone, without so much as leaving a word for me. I waited all day and all night in an agony of apprehension. The next day I started for New Orleans. But I had to take a slow boat. It has been a hideous journey."

"She should have left some word for you. How could you know that she wasn't at the bottom of the river?"

"I can forgive. It was only thoughtlessness."

"But by that thoughtlessness, as well as by the quality of your brief honeymoon, you may judge that you are well quit of her. Well out of the whole mess, indeed. I congratulate you—and her. She acted with decision."

"I had hoped not to insist on this. It must be wounding to a father to hear. But Fernande is my wife already in everything but a legal sense."

"I blush to own it, Mr. Whitman. But I had already guessed as much."

"Then you see why I must reach Fernande, and reach her without delay."

"I see nothing of the kind. Her affair with you had best be forgotten. You have relieved your mind to me. Now say no more about it."

"It cannot be dismissed so lightly."

"It can, and it will. I regret the affair. But it makes no difference so far as the future is concerned."

"The difference is not of your making, Mr. Desmoulins. And it cannot be unmade. The consequences are already on the way."

"The consequences? You don't mean——?"

"I mean just that."

"By God, sir, I could kill you! To stand and leer at me and tell me such a thing!"

"You had to know. You see now. I must marry Fernande."

"By God, no! I'd rather see Fernande and her nameless brat beg in the street than see her married to a Yankee vagabond."

"Take your hands off me. Both your hands. That's better. I see it is useless to talk to you. But I warn you that I shall never give Fernande up. Now or next week, next month or next year, I shall find her, wherever you have hidden her. And when I find her I shall keep her. She belongs to me."

"I am ringing for a servant to show you out, Mr. Whitman. But darkies are slow. While one is coming, I shall have time to give you a very interesting piece of news."

"Tell me where Fernande is. That is the only news which can interest me."

"I shall tell you. I hasten to tell you."

"But why do you look at me like that? What is there of triumph only in knowing where she is?"

"Fernande was married yesterday to a Southern gentleman. Fernande slept last night in a bridal bed. My son-in-law may be a little surprised at the promptness with which his heir is born. But perhaps he, too, knows Fernande."

"I don't believe you! She couldn't—"

"It is a blow, of course. If you weren't a Yankee I could almost find it in my heart to feel sorry for you. You're so far beyond your depth."

"Fernande, my Fernande, who never spoke except of love until that last morning—"

"Ah, boy, there you are! It takes you long enough to answer that bell. I might be murdered in my chair while you're dragging about the corridors. Boy, show Mr. Whitman out the same way you showed him in. And boy, go with him clear to the door."

XIV

1851

NED WILKINS, PFAFF

An off hour at Pfaff's basement restaurant, on Broadway near Bleecker Street, New York. Pfaff's is a great hangout of the elect, but at this moment Ned Wilkins has it to himself. He is now definitely consumptive. Pfaff, a stout, red-faced German, sets down a pint of champagne before him.

"You better have something to eat with that champagne."

"I can't eat, Pfaff. Eating disgusts me."

"I know you ain't much appetite. But the champagne would help you get something down."

"It would solve a good many problems if a man gave up eating."

"A man must eat to live, Mr. Wilkins."

"Granted. But why live?"

"You will have your joke, Mr. Wilkins, though sometimes it ain't so funny, if you ask me."

"A man must be on the right end of a joke to know just how funny it is. The man who owes money, for

[77]

instance, relishes the joke a lot more than the man he owes it to."

"If that's a joke, most newspaper fellers are great jokers. Always want me to wait until Saturday night."

"But do they pay you on Saturday night?"

"If they do, they begin again Sunday to owe me."

"Most of us need the drinks, Pfaff, even if we can't pay for them."

"There was one newspaper feller never owed me money. He never was drunk neither. But he ain't been in lately."

"He has probably gone to Heaven."

"There you go again, Mr. Wilkins, being funny."

"If I might inquire the name of this paragon?"

"This pair o' which?"

"His name, man. His name."

"It was Walt Whitman."

"To be sure it was, Pfaff. He always sat and held his tongue and looked clean and handsome while the rest of us made fools of ourselves."

"He ain't been in for a long time. Some one said he had left here, gone South or something."

"He was away for some time. But he got back. He is living with his father in Brooklyn."

"Then why don't he ever come in here?"

"Because he is too wise to waste his time with a lot of rowdies. But I don't believe he often comes across the river nowadays. He has quit the newspaper business, if business it can be called."

"What is he doing?"

"He builds small houses in Brooklyn, and sells them. His father is a carpenter. Walt works with him."

"He's gone to work as a carpenter?"

"Just so."

"But he wasn't a workman. He was a scholar."

"Newspaper men get into an awful rut, Pfaff. He's wise to make a break. I don't think carpentering is the whole story. I've an idea he is pursuing some end of his own, though I don't know what it may be."

"Have you seen him lately?"

"I ran into him not long ago, on his way home from work. He had his lunch-pail in his hand and a book under his arm. It was a translation of Homer, I noticed. He invited me to come with him some day for a Sunday on the beach. He usually goes off Sundays and spends the day by himself in some remote place."

"I'd like to see Walt again, Mr. Wilkins. How does he look? Same as ever?"

"Not just the same. Of course he was dressed as a working man, wideawake hat and trousers tucked in his boots. But that wasn't the only difference. He seems quieter than he used to. He looks much older, too. His hair and beard are getting quite gray."

"Pshaw, I'm sorry to hear that. I always thought him a handsome fellow. Do you think he's had bad luck of some sort?"

"I think something has happened to him, Pfaff. He is very much changed."

"There ain't so many things can happen to change a man, if you come right down to it. If it ain't drink it's usually a woman."

"I hardly think it's either of those, Pfaff. Walt knew better than to take either drink or women seriously."

"Then he's probably writing a book."

"I wonder if it might be that."

"You may lay your money it is, Mr. Wilkins. I've seen it happen time and again among my customers. Writing a book sets them crazy. They all think everybody is holding their breath waiting for just that book. And Lord, if you had to read them books!"

"I can't imagine what kind of book old Walt would write, if he really set his mind to it. Because, d'ye see, it isn't like him to set his mind very hard to anything."

"If you find out some time, tell Pfaff."

"Is the last drop of that champagne gone, Pfaff? How soon it goes! What's the setback?"

"Never mind paying today. We drink on Walt. If you see him again tell him to come in here. He needn't order anything if he comes. I'd be glad just to see him."

"You're twittering with curiosity, aren't you, Pfaff? On second thoughts, though, I believe you're going to be disappointed. Walt would never turn his life upside-down just to write a book. It's much more likely to be a woman."

"It couldn't be a woman. Because if it was a woman she'd take him."

"How can you be sure of that, Pfaff?"

"I've eyes, ain't I? You can tell just to look at him. Any woman would take him."

XV

1852

NED WILKINS, WALT WHITMAN

*The beach at Coney Island on a fine
summer Sunday. Coney Island in
1852 presents nothing but a wide
stretch of sand, sea and sky. In the
midst of the immensity Walt is strip-
ping for a swim. Ned Wilkins sub-
sides into a sun-warmed hollow beside the lunch-basket.*

"Sure you won't go for a swim today, Ned?"

"I'm no swimmer."

"Then why not just souse in the waves? There's
nothing like a dip in salt water for making a man
tingle all over."

"The ocean looks a little overwhelming. I think I'd
rather lie on the sand and see if I can't get thoroughly
warm for once."

"Help yourself to my books. You will find them
inside the basket."

"Thank you, I will have a look at them. I want to
see what sort of reading you waste your time on. Read
a good deal these days, don't you?"

"More than I ever have since I was a boy and
cared to do nothing else but read."

"Well, it helps a man to get through the day. What
the devil is this, Walt? 'The Lily and the Bee.' What
lily and what bee?"

"Oh, that's a book by Samuel Warren, the *Blackwood* novelist."

"The fellow who wrote 'Ten Thousand a Year?'"

"The same fellow. He wrote this for the Crystal
Palace exhibition."

"Damned if I can see how the exhibition would
benefit. What is the stuff, anyhow? It looks like poetry,
but it isn't. They've spilled all the exclamation-points
in the shop on one page. Listen to how it goes:

" 'In dusky, rainless Egypt now!
   Mysterious memories come crowding round—
   From mighty Mizraim to Ibrahim—
   Abraham! Joseph! Pharaoh's plagues!
   Shepherd kings! Sesostris!
   Cambyses! Xerxes! Alexander! Ptolemies! Antony! Cleo-
      patra!'

Er, yes indeed! If Antony, by all means Cleopatra.
Where was I?

" '—Cleopatra! Cæsar—'

Cæsar too! But we get on more respectable ground
in the next line.

" 'Isis! Osiris! Temples! Sphinxes! Obelisks! Alexandria!
   The Pyramids!
   The Nile!
   NAPOLEON! NELSON!
   —Behold, my son, quoth the Royal Mother, this ancient
      wondrous country—destined scene of mighty doings—

perchance of conflict, deadly, tremendous, such as the
world has never seen, nor warrior dreamed of.'

"I say, Walt, this is fascinating. But what's it all
about?"

"Don't you get the swing of it?"

"If it swings, it swings a little beyond my reach.
Ah, here we are again! Let's see where we get on this
start."

" 'A unit unperceived,
    I sink into the living stream again!—
    Nave, Transept, Aisles and Galleries,
    ·Pacing untired: insatiate!
    Touchstone of character! capacity! and knowledge!
    Spectacle, now lost in the spectators: then spectators in the
        spectacle.'

"Hates himself, don't he?"

"Don't go on, Ned, if it bores you."

"On the contrary, it fascinates me. I say, Walt,
here's a plum for you!

" 'Poor Bee! Dost thou see ME?
    And note my speculations,
    Thinking so curiously, all so confident!
    Of thee, thy Beings, Doings!
    —MYSELF! The While!
    Unconsciously contemplated by Intelligence, unseen!
    Transcending mortal man
    Yet far himself from the Supreme
    As finite from the Infinite!'

"That's very good, Walt. The author looks down
on the bee from the height of *Blackwood's Magazine*

as God looks down on the author. But there must be some one somewhere looking down on God too. That's a proper revenge on God, even if it hasn't much to do with the Crystal Palace exhibition."

"If you're not going in the water, Ned, don't you want to smoke? I trust you brought along some cigars."

"I brought a day's supply. I knew you weren't to be relied on for tobacco. Say, Walt, how ruddy your whole body is!"

"It's a good body. I feel friendly toward my body when it tingles to the wash of salt water. Here goes!"

"If had a body like that, and could swim like that —I'd swim."

"Down at Peconic Bay last summer the natives used to watch as I passed down the street. There was a head at every window of every house, as if I were a procession. But when I went in the water they not only watched, but gathered. There would sometimes be a whole crowd of natives on the beach to see me go in."

"What were you doing down at Peconic Bay, Walt?"

"Swimming. Or floating on my back, like this. Even better than the thrust of swimming is lying on one's back and going with the motion of the water."

"It's one way of getting through the days, I suppose. But it seems dreadfully amphibious."

"I'm not quite a fish, Ned. When I come out of the water, I generally write in my notebook."

"You keep a notebook? I hadn't suspected you of so much system."

"You say 'system' as if to be systematic were a crime. But how else is a fellow to get the better of the thoughts that assail him, except by writing them down as they come?"

"Have you a notebook along today?"

"Right there under your hand."

"I see nothing but the confounded 'Lily and the Bee.' "

"Look inside the cover."

"You mean these few sheets of paper stitched together?"

"That's it. That's my present notebook."

"Let's have a look at what assails you when you come out of the water. H'm. 'Get from Mr. Arkhurst'—whoever he is—'the names of all insects. Interweave a train of thought suitable.' That's evidently what your friend Warren did with the names of Egyptian history. Only he carelessly omitted the train of thought. But suppose you did interweave it. What would you have?"

"A poem, Ned."

"A poem! Good God! I thought poems were handed down by the Muse, not built up from the grasshoppers. I see, though, that the process still bothers you. Farther on in the notebook you say, 'How shall my eye separate the beauty of the blossoming buckwheat field from the stalks and heads of tangible matter? How shall I know what life is except as I see it in the flesh?' How, indeed? You may well ask."

"Close the book, Ned, if it brings no enlightenment. Perhaps it means nothing to any eye but mine."

"It may not enlighten, but it interests me vastly. Here's another entry: 'A Poem—Theme: Be Happy. Going forth, seeing all the beautiful perfect things.'

I like that, Walt. 'The beautiful perfect things.' The ocean and the sky, and your own pink body cutting the water. Only—"

"Yes, Ned?"

"Only if you see the beautiful perfect things and are happy, why not let it go at that? Why trouble to write about them?"

"Because I'm not quite happy, Ned, nor ever quite at rest, until the poem comes."

"You are really going to write poetry, then?"

"I have written poems."

"Many poems?"

"Twelve of them. One longish. The others not so long."

"You have written twelve poems? That's real news."

"Say, if you like, that I have written twenty-four poems. For I have done the twelve poems twice."

"You've written them twice all through? Well, now what are you going to do with them?"

"I can't say as yet. I write a thing in pieces as it occurs to me. I write in my room at my father's, on the ferry or bus, often on the beach alone. Then I copy all the fragments together, and lay the completed poem aside. Some time after I take it up and read it. If it reads without perceptible jar, seems to say what I mean it to say, I call it done."

"Sounds as if it might be. But it's slow doing. No wonder you've accomplished only twelve poems in two years."

"Not that, as a matter of fact. So far only one of the twelve pleases me as it stands."

"You're a rum one, Walt. What does your family think of all this writing?"

"They pay no attention. They're used to my scribbling. If they think anything, they think I'm writing more lectures."

"Do you write lectures too?"

"I've written a whole barrel of lectures. A couple of years ago I had a great idea of lecturing. But somehow the idea wore out before I got anything done about it."

"I believe you were wise to abandon that idea. When I see you swaying up and down with the waves, it strikes me that rhythm is your element."

"There is rhythm in everything that carries us, Ned. Rhythm not only in the up and down of the waves, but in the motion of the ferry-boat, the railroad-train, the flight of birds. If I could catch that rhythm and make it more rhythmical I should have something."

"If you could only catch it, that ought to be enough for you. A man as full of life as you are can get along without mere literature."

"Oh, the mereness of mere literature! No one feels that more than I do, Ned. Yet if we had not passed through literature, the very rhythm of the sea, the very color of the sunshine, would not come to us as they do."

"You mean that in the very swing and dash of the water you are reminded, say, of Homer?"

"Well, not of Homer today. Just this minute I was thinking of some lines from Tupper's 'Proverbial Philosophy.' That's right, laugh if you want to. Your laughter is infrequent, Ned. Thank Martin Tupper for it."

"I really know very little about him. I suppose I was laughing just at his name. Tupper isn't such a good name for a poet. By the way, Walt Whitman is a very good name. I suppose that is why you have shortened it. You used to call yourself Walter."

"Listen, Ned, and I'll shout a little Tupper at you.

" 'Where are the nobles of Nineveh, and mitred rulers of Babylon?
Where are the lords of Edom, and the royal pontiffs of Thebais?
The golden Satrap, and the Tetrarch—the Hun, and the Druid, and the Celt?
The merchant princes of Phœnicia, and the minds that fashioned Elephanta?
Alas, for the poet hath forgotten them; and lo! they are outcasts of Memory;
Alas, that they are withered leaves, sapless and fallen from the chaplet of fame.
Speak, Etruria, whose bones be these, entombed with costly care,—
Tell out, Herculaneum, the titles that have sounded in thy palaces,—
Lycian Xanthus, thy citadels are mute, and the honour of their architects hath died;
Copan and Palenque, dreamy ruins in the West, the forest hath swallowed up your sepultures;
Syracuse—how silent of the past! Carthage, thou art blotted from remembrance!
Egypt, wondrous shores, ye are buried in the sandhills of forgetfulness.'

"How's that for Martin Tupper, eh?"

"Egypt again, Walt! Can't you stay off Egypt?"

"I can stay on the shores of Long Island, and within the spaces of Manhattan. Let me once get the rhythm of Manhattan, and the mighty states inland and seaboard—"

"And the trick will be turned, will it, Walt?"

"At least the substance will be there. Then the main thing is to leave out the stock poetic touches. A simple plate-glass style is the thing that I must try for."

"But what is to show through the plate-glass when you have it?"

"Beauty to the ear, beauty to the brain, beauty to the heart, beauty to the time and place. That is all that can show through the perfectest poetry."

"You aim at the perfectest poetry?"

"I take what comes to me, and let it keep coming."

"You even encourage it?"

"It does not come without encouragement. I emerge now to bake upon the sands. When I have baked a while, let's eat lunch."

"And after lunch?"

"After lunch Homer, if you like. But Homer stands completed, and these lesser men you laugh at are feeling for something."

"I wish they may get it, Walt. You emerge like Neptune, with salt spray on your hair and beard. Why don't you shave that gray beard? Its loss would make you look younger."

"Let youth pass when the time comes for its passing."

"Do you feel that you will get the rhythm of youth better when it has passed?"

"I may. Or I may get something else more important. Now be silent for just a minute. Let us watch the curve of the seashore, and the waves that caress it and then withdraw."

"Giving place to other waves, Walt. Rhythms go on —until they make a man a little sleepy."

XVI

1855

JAMES ROME, ANDREW ROME

The printing-office of the brothers
Rome, at the corner of Fulton and
Cranberry Streets, Brooklyn. The
brothers are in the little back room
on the ground floor, discussing a
phenomenon that is soon to puzzle
wiser heads.

"Did Walt Whitman come in this afternoon, James?"

"He's downstairs now, setting type. He ran off the proof of his Preface and his first poem. It's there on the table. He's setting up another poem."

"Insists on setting up his own poems, does he? Expects us to take that off the bill, perhaps."

"He says he likes the feeling and look of the type. He changes things, too, as he goes along."

"He don't change 'em enough, James. Let's have a look at his first poem. H'm, Listen to this!

" 'I celebrate myself,
And what I assume you shall assume.'

"He assumes a good deal when he calls that poetry."

"I know it sounds like crazy stuff, Andy. But the Preface is better. I read his Preface all through. That tells what he's getting at."

"Must take a lot of telling."

"Listen while I read you a sentence. 'Of the traits of the brotherhood of writers savans musicians inventors and artists nothing is finer than silent defiance advancing from new free form.' Now, don't that say it?"

"Maybe it does, James. But don't Walt never use no commas?"

"I suppose his punctuation is part of his freedom."

"Or part of his 'silent defiance.' What's this tintype doing here?"

"He's going to have a cut made from it. That's to go in the book."

"That to go in the book? With his undershirt showing?"

"The undershirt was an accident, like. He told me about the day it was taken. He was lounging up the street, free and easy, same as he always does, with his hat pushed back and his trousers tucked in the tops of his boots—"

"And not in any hurry, I'll be bound."

"That fellow Gabriel Harrison, who takes pictures, was standing in his doorway. When he saw Walt he sang out, 'Old man, old man! Come here. Come right upstairs with me this minute.' Walt hesitated. He didn't know what the fellow was after. Harrison says, 'Come on. I'm dying for something to do, and you've a face that cries for the camera.' "

"But look here, James, Walt ain't an old man."

"He tries to let on like he is. It's a part of his queerness, I guess."

"Strikes me this is kind of a sulky-looking picture. But if he wants it to go in his book, that's his business.

He pays his bills pretty prompt. I'll say that for him."

"It's going to be a queer book, Andy. But if his queerness strikes other people's queerness, it may do."

"Has he made up his mind what he is going to call it?"

"Sure. Didn't he tell you? He's going to call it 'Leaves of Grass.' "

"That's the same as he told me. But I was in hopes he might have changed his mind. That's nothing to call a book. 'Bale of Hay' would be as much to the point. Anyhow, grass don't grow in leaves. It grows in blades."

"That's another thing I said to him, Andy. But he said he thought 'leaves' sounded better. He reads all his poems over out loud, to see how they sound."

"Is he going to follow every buyer home with his book and read it out loud to them?"

"He's using a beautiful big page for his book, eight inches by eleven. That allows his long lines to be printed without a break."

"Ah, he's got a feeling for type. I'll say that for him. He learned his trade good too, from old man Hartshorne. But a printer should stick to his case, I say, and not try to be a poet."

"Walt is a writer, though, you know. He has worked on newspapers."

"And for that matter he's working building houses. But only for his father. I don't suppose anyone else would stand for the kind of carpenter work he would do."

"I guess his carpentering days are past, then. I hear old man Whitman is very low."

"Sick, is he? Pshaw, I didn't know that."

"He's had a stroke or something, and they've taken him out to his old home near Huntington."

"Well, his widow will have plenty of sons to look after her. George and Jeff are good boys, too. Solid fellows with no nonsense about 'em."

"That's what my wife's sister says. She lives next door to the Whitmans. She says, though, that Walt is his mother's favorite."

"There's another brother, too, that's a plumb idiot."

"That would be the youngest, Eddie."

"They're a queer lot, though I like the old lady."

"I suppose there's worse things than queerness, Andy."

"Suppose ahead, James. Just don't you go printing your picture in your undershirt, and a lot of so-called poems that sound like the names of railroads strung together."

"Like the names of railroads? That ain't bad. Some of Walt's poems do sound like the name of one railroad after another. Maybe that's why I kind of like 'em. If I'm stopped at a crossing to let a freight-train go by, I always read the names of the railroads off'm the cars. It makes a kind of poetry, now I come to think of it."

"The more fool you, James, if you think that's poetry."

"Besides, Andy, when the brakeman couples the cars, that joins all the different names together into one string, don't you see?"

"It may, James. It may. But when the brakeman couples the cars together, that don't start the train."

XVII

1855

GEORGE WHITMAN, WALT WHITMAN

In the small room at the Rome broth-ers' printing-office sits the author of the lately published "Leaves of Grass." He is surrounded by a welter of newspaper clippings, letters, and poems in manuscript and proof. In from the bright September sunshine comes the author's brother George, a young man with no nonsense about him.

"Hello, Walt. I thought I might find you here."

"Hello, George. Won't you sit down?"

"I'm on my way up to Mother's. I thought you might want to walk along."

"I'm not quite ready to go yet. I had a visitor this afternoon, and he stayed talking a long time."

"Didn't you do your share of the talking?"

"He came to hear what I had to say. Came because he had read and admired 'Leaves of Grass.' "

"And wanted to find out what you meant by it, did he?"

"Emerson advised him to come. He is a young Vir-ginian named Moncure Conway. Lately he has been living in Concord to be near Emerson."

"Have you ever answered Emerson's letter about your book? You got it a long time ago."

"It came in July. But does one answer such a princely letter with a dozen lines scrawled on a sheet of note-paper? My answer to Emerson is to be a new edition of my book, with new poems, many new poems."

"I don't see why you want to waste your money on a new edition. You couldn't sell the first one."

" 'Leaves of Grass' is a book only for those who can accept it, George. They may be few, but they have been enthusiastic."

"I know you were all set up because Bryant came across the river to see you, and Emerson wrote you that he liked your book."

"Emerson did not pause at a lukewarm liking. Emerson wrote me, 'I find it the most extraordinary piece of wit and wisdom that America has yet contributed.' Emerson said, 'I greet you at the beginning of a great career.' "

"What Emerson says won't sell many books. He got even his own copy free, didn't he?"

"I mailed it to him."

"And the reviews have been so damn bad."

"Not so bad as they might have been."

"Have you seen the review in the new *Putnam's Monthly?*"

"I have it here, George. Read it out to me, if you like."

"I don't see why you should want to hear it."

"I get the sense of a thing better when it is read out loud. I always test my poems so. Go on. I am listening."

"Oh, if you insist! It begins by calling your book

[96]

'a curious and lawless collection of poems, neither in rhyme nor in blank verse, but in a sort of excited prose, broken into lines without any attempt at measure or regularity.' Just so. Farther along it says that the poems 'may briefly be described as a compound of the New England transcendentalist and the New York rowdy. A fireman or omnibus driver, who had intelligence enough to absorb the speculations of that school of thought which culminated at Boston some fifteen or eighteen years ago, and resources of expression to put them forth again in a form of his own, with sufficient self-conceit and contempt for public taste to affront all usual propriety of diction, might have written this gross yet elevated, this superficial yet profound, this preposterous yet somehow fascinating book.' "

"You couldn't ask for more than that, George. It calls 'Leaves of Grass' elevated, profound, and fascinating."

"It calls you a New York rowdy."

"Perhaps I am, George. I'm a ferry-rat at least. And that touch about the omnibus driver is good. I have driven a Broadway omnibus more than once."

"Surprised you haven't tried to steer the ferry-boat too."

"I have steered a ferry many times, to relieve the regular pilot. We would exchange jobs for a while. The pilot would read my Homer while I steered his boat."

"I wouldn't trust you with any boat that belonged to me."

"You would be quite right not to, George. Just after 'Leaves of Grass' was published I piloted the ferry bang into another boat. Since then I haven't

cared so much about steering. I prefer to let the pilot
have my Walter Scott to take home with him."

"I tell you, Walt, it's all right for a young fellow
to try his hand at a lot of different things. But you're
getting on, you know. Now that Father's gone, I
thought you might take over his carpenter business.
You could make money at it. You're not such a good
workman as poor Father was, but people usually take
to you."

"Let me tell you something, George. When 'Leaves
of Grass' came out it was discussed at the New York
Press by men who had known me. It was universally
condemned. Only one man stood up for it, Ned Wilkins."

"The fellow with the awfully weak voice? I shouldn't
think his defense would amount to much."

"Ned has a gallant spirit housed in a sick body.
Perhaps it was the healthiness of 'Leaves of Grass'
that drew him. Perhaps he defended it out of affection for me. Anyhow, he was in a minority. A tempest
of disapproval set in. When I saw what was happening, I went down to my old haunts on Peconic
Bay."

"I remember your going. I can't make out what
you went for."

"I bathed and fished for a week, and gave myself
up to the pure healthy life of the body. In that week
my difficulty solved itself."

"How?"

"I went to work on new poems."

"Walt, I can't make out about these so-called poems
of yours. Damn it, I think you have talent enough
to write right. What are you up to, anyhow?"

"That's just the question. What am I up to?"

"I say, Walt, have you nothing to say?"

"Nothing to say, George. I did what I did because I did it. That's the whole secret."

"You're as stubborn as hell, Walt."

"I let other people explain me. Have you seen the *Democratic Review?*"

"The *Democratic Review* ought to be good to you. You used to have a lot of stories in it."

"Listen to what the *Democratic* says of me: 'An American bard at last! You have come in good time, Walt Whitman! In opinions, in manners, in costumes, in books, in the aims of occupancy of life, in associates, in poems, conformity to all unnatural and tainted customs passes without remark, while perfect naturalness, health, faith, self-reliance, and all primal expressions of the manliest love and friendship, subject one to the stare and controversy of the world.' "

"That's not so bad. Kind of seems as if I had heard something like it somewhere before."

"Then there's the *Phrenological Journal.* That contains a comparison of 'Leaves of Grass' with Tennyson's 'Maud.' They would naturally be friendly, because the firm that publishes the *Phrenological Journal* is to undertake the new edition of 'Leaves of Grass.' "

"I'm glad to hear that. If you get a regular publisher, and try to sell your book in the regular way, it may do better."

"It may. But my book is very close to me. I fear I shall lose something in losing control over it."

"Any other good reviews, Walt?"

"Here is yesterday's Brooklyn *Times.*"

"And a good long piece about you, I see. This is

queer. How did they happen to find out so much about you?"

"I am fairly well known in Brooklyn, George."

"It begins, 'To give judgment on real poems, one needs an account of the poet himself. Very devilish to some, and very divine to some, will appear the poet of these new poems, the "Leaves of Grass"; an attempt as they are, of a naive, masculine, affectionate, contemplative, sensual, imperious person, to cast into literature not only his own grit and arrogance, but his own flesh and form, undraped, regardless of models, regardless of modesty or law, and ignorant or silently scornful, as at first appears, of all except his own presence and experience, and all outside the fiercely loved land of his birth, and the birth of his parents, and their parents for several generations before him.' This *is* queer."

"Go on, George."

"It goes on with a long description of you, how you look, and what you do and what you don't do. And it ends, 'There you have Walt Whitman, the begetter of new offspring out of literature, taking with easy nonchalance the chances of its present reception, and, through all misunderstandings and distrusts, the chances of its future reception—preferring always to speak for himself rather than have others speak for him.'"

"'That says a good deal, doesn't it?"

" 'Preferring always to speak for himself rather than have others speak for him.' Walt Whitman, you wrote that review yourself!"

"And if I did, George?"

"And that one in the *Democratic Review,* that says

you have come in good time. Did you write that, too?"

"Perhaps."

"I suppose it's all right if you want to do it. But seems to me if I wrote a book that no one else could say anything good about, I wouldn't go praising it myself on the sly."

"I didn't think I should have to do it, George. I thought I had written a book so crystal-clear that it could not be misunderstood. I wrote 'Leaves of Grass' five times all through, and five times I discarded the finished result as not good enough. The sixth version I printed."

"You've stuck to it. I give you credit for that."

"And what is the result of my sticking? The fellows on top do not want me at any price, not even as a gift. Some of the copies of 'Leaves of Grass' that I sent as presents were returned to me, and I have heard that others were put in the fire. As for the people, the crowd, the vast unreading democratic mass, I have no way of reaching them."

"The people who don't read don't read. I should think you would have known that to begin with."

"I sometimes think of going out and around, and reading my poems in public. I feel that the people would understand, would listen, would get to know what I am about."

"Walt, you wouldn't really do such a thing?"

"Very likely I shall not do it. Yet it would serve the purpose if I did."

"But think of the chance it would give people to make fun of you!"

"No greater chance than they have had already, and availed themselves of."

"See here, Walt, I thought better of you than this. You're howling like a scalded baby. Yet you would insist on turning the kettle over on yourself."

"I challenged accepted opinion, but I failed to allow for its malice. The enemy wants for nothing better or more than simply, without remorse, to brush me without compunction or mercy, out of sight, out of hearing."

"Then they've got their work cut out for them. That's all I've got to say."

"So they have, George. So they have. I've the good Dutch stubbornness that you twit me with. And I've Emerson on my side, on my side with no if's or but's. Emerson himself says that one with God is a majority. When Emerson is the one, one with God is a great majority indeed."

"You're feeling better, aren't you, Walt? You look more cheerful all of a sudden."

"I've just had an idea. Where's my hat? Somewhere in this mess, I suppose."

"Are you coming along up to Mother's?"

"No. Tell Mother I shall be late. I'm going over to New York. I want to see Dana."

"You mean Dana of the *Sun?*"

"That's the man. Charles A. Dana. I must have his advice."

"I don't know what you're got up your sleeve now, Walt. And if you've set your mind on doing anything, a word of caution would be as good as wasted."

"Worse than wasted, George. Yet it is caution that is taking me to Dana now. Caution becomes me at this point. I am beginning to see that I have a long road ahead."

XVIII

1857

RALPH WALDO EMERSON, WALT WHITMAN

In the dining-room of an American-plan hotel in New York the Sage of Concord is sitting down to dinner with a man whom he always looks up when he comes to New York.

"We must both be ready to enjoy our dinner, Mr. Whitman. That was a long walk, though leisurely."

"I often stroll about in that way hour after hour, viewing the thronging life of the city streets. When I am weary I climb to the top of a bus. The bus drivers all know me. Some of them carry an extra cushion for me on the seat beside them."

"I have every respect for those Broadway bus drivers. It must take a great deal of skill to tool a bus through those crowded streets."

"They are fine individuals, Mr. Emerson. Great studies I have found them also. They have immense qualities, largely animal: eating, drinking, women—"

"Ah, yes!"

"Yet great personal pride too, and in most cases simple good-will and honor. There may be a few slouches among them. But not many. Not many. Most of them are to be depended on for comradeship, and even for simple affection."

"These casual relations must make great demands on your time, Mr. Whitman."

"But I have all the time there is. I long ago said farewell to all regular occupation, to business and money making. I do a little newspaper work to pay my way. But almost every day I find leisure to come over to New York, stroll about, perhaps ride on a bus, perhaps go to the theatre, eat a plain dinner somewhere, and return late to my mother's in Brooklyn."

"Your mother still lives in Brooklyn?"

"She has continued there since my father's death two years ago. Some of her children are always with her. One of these days I must take you over to see my mother. She would like to do you the simple honors of her house."

"I should be charmed to meet a poet's mother."

"She never thinks of me as a poet. To her I am just Walt, to be forgiven for my poetry because I am on the whole a good son. So, here comes our dinner. It looks abundant, at least."

"We have talked much today, Mr. Whitman. But so far you have said nothing of your own proper work. Surely you are busy with more poems?"

"I have written more poems, many more. I write, rewrite, discard. For every poem that I print I throw aside three. But 'Leaves of Grass' is growing all the time."

"You do not consider that it has yet assumed its final shape?"

"It changes under my hands."

"Then you plan yet another edition?"

"I shall make a new edition when I can find a new publisher."

"I remember that you published the first edition yourself. Had you a publisher for the second? I can recall no name of a publisher on the title-page."

"I had a publisher, though no name appeared. But prosecution was threatened, and Fowler and Wells dropped the book at the first hint of trouble. I think they seized the pretext to drop it. Their attitude was grudging."

"But their edition had sold well?"

"The sale was small."

"That was too bad. Too bad indeed."

"You say that in a friendly manner, Mr. Emerson. But perhaps you are not ill pleased that the second edition halted early. Moncure Conway came to see me after the issue, and let me understand that you were indignant at having your name publicly associated with my book."

"Conway told you that? I remember now, Conway was with me when I received your book through the mail. But he must have misunderstood my attitude. I was not indignant at all. I was simply startled at seeing my own name stare at me from the very cover of your book."

"I used your generous letter on Dana's advice. You know Charles Dana, of the New York *Sun?* He told me by all means to run it in my book. As for putting that one sentence on the cover, that was my own idea, and I am afraid not a good one. Yet conceive how important your words were to me. Over your honored name you had written, 'I greet you at the beginning of a great career.' "

"I do not retract that greeting. As for your use of it on the back of your book, let us say no more about it. I am happy to be associated with you in the public mind. Yet I was by no means the most militant of your champions. Henry Thoreau carried your book around Concord like a red rag."

"Thoreau came to see me, perhaps two years ago. He has come more than once since. On that very first visit he said, 'Whitman, have you any idea that you are bigger and outside the average, that you may perhaps have immense significance?' I did not answer at once. Thoreau went on, 'Yet there is much in you to which I cannot accommodate myself. The defect may be mine, but the objections are there.' "

"And what did you say to that?"

"I couldn't say much. You see, I thought the defect was in him."

"Henry is an honest man, Mr. Whitman, and one who never stops to count the cost when it is a question of his duty."

"I grant his courage, and his strength of will. But is not his view of his duty just a little near-sighted?"

"Henry is not to be blamed because he was born myopic."

"In a literal physical sense, Mr. Emerson, near-sightedness is often due not to natural defect but to habit. I note that the eyes of country and seafaring persons focus commonly and easily at a distance. The eyes of city men focus at a foot or so, the eyes of scholars sometimes at six inches."

"Then you are charging that Henry has the defects of his class. Yet his whole life has been one long struggle to avoid classifying himself."

"Bronson Alcott came to see me, too. Indeed he and Thoreau once came together. Thoreau was in every way a bigger man than Alcott, more direct, immediate, gathered to a point. He struck me as having the skeleton of happiness, even if his happiness had no flesh upon it. But Thoreau had the same manner as Alcott."

"You mean a sort of aloofness?"

"Well, I got the impression that they were willing to come only so far, and meant me to see it. If they came an inch beyond their self-imposed boundaries, they felt it must result in disaster."

"Doubtless, Mr. Whitman, a dedicated life makes a man a coward. I feel in my own case that it has deprived me of something. Within the walls of my study I am not only fully at home but freely content. But turn me out into the dirt and noises of the street, and I am ill at ease. I sometimes envy the nonchalance of the street urchin."

"Or of the street ruffian, like the specimen you have before you now?"

"You speak in jest, Whitman—Mr. Whitman. If I relish this particular jest, it is only because there lies behind it a very beautiful earnest. You are right in assuming that I do not mix easily with mankind at large. The first time I sought you out and we walked together as we have walked today, I was fairly thunderstruck by the way common persons saluted you. Bus driver and bootblack, car conductor and ferryman, not only greeted you, but greeted you as an intimate."

"Did they shout, 'Hello, Walt?' Many of them do. Not all, but many."

"That was what they shouted. But once I had got over the shock of that casual address, I envied you the freedom with which men approach you. But may not that very freedom have its drawbacks?"

"What drawbacks do you mean?"

"Don't you fear now and then—just now and then—that your freedom, your ease, your nonchalance with men, may be misunderstood?"

"Mr. Emerson, do you misunderstand it?"

"I, my dear fellow? I see it for what it is. It is beautiful."

"It is not commonly misunderstood. And suppose once in a while it was? That would not be the only thing about me that is misunderstood."

"True, true. Yet apparently you thrive on misunderstanding."

"I must, if I am to thrive at all. Yet I realize that except in the size of the tempest I have raised, my experience has been no worse than another's. It is what we have to expect if we will set things down in writing."

"The very act of writing, or at any rate the fact of publishing, takes for granted a sympathetic reader. You feel we are not justified in taking so much for granted?"

"The happy accident justifies us—when it occurs."

"You would hardly look for that accident in the case of a regular critic, if your experience has been at all like mine, Mr. Whitman. I for my part have found the critics not unfriendly. But I seem to mystify them."

"I antagonize the critics, rile them, make them mad.

Of course I mystify them too. But they don't know it."

"Let us leave the professional critics, and speak of pleasanter topics. You mentioned the happy accident which gives us a perfect reader."

"It takes a rare mixture of qualities, Mr. Emerson, to make even a good reader. But no man, however rarely mixed, can be a perfect reader except of the few books that chance to suit his temperament, to affirm and echo the voice that he hears in his own heart."

"Then you question the universal appeal even of the greatest books?"

"Let me give you a homely illustration. Last week there was a man came North from Georgia on purpose to see me, a philosopher-farmer named Johnson, though better doubtless at philosophy than at farming. He had taken 'Leaves of Grass' to his heart, had read and quoted it until it became a byword with his family, had at length come rushing North to see what the author was like."

"A tribute, Mr. Whitman. The spontaneous tribute of a natural man."

"It was a tribute, to be sure. But that isn't what I'm getting at. Says this Johnson to me, 'When I'm down home I often take my gun and go gunning for possum, and when I come along to a spot where one has been, I say to myself, "The old varmint's been here as well as I." So when I read Whitman I keep coming to ideas familiar to me, and I say, same as I did of the possum, "The old varmint's been here before me."' And by and bye I come to the conclusion that there warn't no place where he hadn't been.' Thus Johnson delivered himself, and I think made his point."

"He made his point, yes, though the metaphor seems not quite right. A telling figure of speech, but the application is upside-down. Has that been your own experience of books?"

"Pretty much my own experience. The book from which I can drink deep is the book that affirms me to myself. Homer, Shakespeare, are right and true, because for all the differences of place and time and custom they speak to the man Walt Whitman."

"Perhaps that does not quite cover the relation of books and readers. But it explains something that has puzzled me. I have found you a copious book man, a readier knower of conventional things than I should have supposed."

"Good literature has its place outside the scholar's study. During the years that I worked as a carpenter, while 'Leaves of Grass' was germinating, I took a book to work as regularly as I took my lunch-pail. It was so that I first read Emerson's Essays."

"I am surprised, Mr. Whitman, not that a man should read because he likes to read, but that a man should know so much and live it down. I don't say that by way of flattery at all. I should say it just as readily to any man like you who had never written a book. But meeting you is a peculiar refreshment to me. It puts into my tissue something needed, but something that I do not seem to get in my own environment."

"A different focus, perhaps?"

"I should rather say a certain spontaneity, like the spontaneity of Nature itself. Yet you are not foolishly impulsive."

"I am a little overcautious, if anything, Mr. Emerson. But caution, even overcaution, is necessary if a man would carry through his work in this world, if he would remain faithful to his initial purpose. There is everything to tempt a man to stray, little to hold him steadfast. Yet to stick must be at last its own satisfaction."

"Indeed, indeed it must. Integrity is all. A man who does not live according to his lights, who trims his sail to the current breeze, is as many times dead as he is untrue."

"Amen to that! Amen to that!"

"But there are pleasant distractions beside the way, and a good dinner with a good friend not the least of them. Now what shall we have to top off with?"

"Here is something in the way of topping, it appears. But what are these?"

"I don't know. We will see."

"But if we don't like them——"

"Then we will eat what is set before us, asking no questions."

"Mr. Emerson, as usual you express an ideal, though in this case it happens not to be my ideal as well."

"But, Mr. Whitman, as usual my ideal yields to your strong sense of reality. Would you mind calling back the waiter?"

XIX

1858

FANNY WRIGHT, WALT WHITMAN

An anteroom at Tammany Hall. The brilliant Mrs. Wright, editor of the Free Inquirer, *has just concluded one of her Sunday afternoon lectures. She has shut herself in here to escape from her too sympathetic hearers. But one bolder than the others, or better informed as to her whereabouts, finds her anyhow.*

"A newspaper man to interview the speaker. May I come in?"

"Come in quickly, Walt, and shut the door. I am hiding here until everybody has gone."

"That's no way to do. Come out and mingle with the crowd. You ought to hear every echo of the enthusiasm you create."

"The audience was attentive today. I have never had a better."

"The audience was what you made them. You were at your own best this afternoon. Then, why not let them tell you about it?"

"The enthusiasm is for the speaker. The woman is better hidden."

[113]

"As regards the run of your hearers, you are well hidden. I believe they think of you as existing in a vacuum from Sunday to Sunday, and of the *Free Inquirer* as accomplishing itself by a miracle."

"That is precisely what I want them to think."

"You are wrong if you do. I am one of your best hearers, Fanny. Sunday after Sunday I sit in your audience and listen to the eloquent stream of your speech, watch your flashing eyes and fine free gestures. Yet when I walk home with you through the dusk of a winter afternoon, and perhaps sit for an hour afterward beside your fire, I find you always more flashing, more inspiring, and somehow more of a personage than ever."

"You find what you seek. You always encourage me to shine. But you won't find me very scintillating tonight. I'm afraid I'm tired."

"You are worse than tired tonight. You are troubled."

"Only more of the old trouble, Walt."

"You mean your husband?"

"Not so much my husband. He seldoms bothers me since our separation. He protested as a matter of form. I think he was secretly glad to be rid of me."

"Then it is his relatives who annoy you?"

"His ghastly mother, sisters, brother."

"They still have your child?"

"They have my child and my money. Think of the unspeakable injustice that money does me. If I were a poor woman who had to earn a miserable pinched living by sewing or going out to work, they would let me take the child. And oh, Walt, I could provide for him and care for him!"

"Indeed you could. I know you could."

"It is three years since I have even seen him. And he is so little still, so in need of tenderness. Only because there is money involved they keep him from me."

"Can nothing be done about it?"

"Legally the child is his father's. I have no redress. There was a fresh turn of the screw yesterday. They demand now that I give up my lectures, and cease to disgrace their name with the *Free Inquirer.*"

"Fanny, you wouldn't do that?"

"I won't. They have overreached themselves this time. Between my lectures and my writing I make enough to live on. They won't let me have my child anyhow. I shall keep on as I have set out."

"Spoken like a dauntless woman. And like a free spirit if ever there was one."

"I didn't mean to talk so much about my troubles. Heaven knows I'm sick of the whole subject. But you brought it on yourself. Now let's have turn about. How is Walt Whitman getting on?"

"He is getting on famously. This is his third year as editor of the Brooklyn *Daily Times.*"

"You know I wasn't asking about the mere livelihood."

"I don't know why you shouldn't ask even about that. Since my father died three years ago, my job on the *Times* has been important to my mother. The best part of any man is his mother. You would simply love mine."

"Let me meet her some time."

"Anyhow, my work for the *Times* has refuted a persistent calumny."

"What calumny?"

"That Walt Whitman couldn't hold a steady job."

"That isn't a calumny. It's a boast."

"As a matter of fact, I haven't usually held a steady job. But it was because I chose not to."

"A man must be assured of the means of living, Walt. But once those are taken care of, the question becomes what does he do with his life. What comes out of him as a result of all the bread and beef that goes in?"

"Out of my bread and beef will some day come a new edition of my poems. It will be much larger than the two earlier."

"Is it to include the new poems that I like so well, 'Of the terrible doubt of appearances,' and 'I hear it was charged against me that I sought to destroy institutions'?"

"It is to include everything that passes the test of my own judgment. You know that has always been my scheme, to include in my poems a complete person."

"Will readers ever see what you are driving at? Readers are so stupid!"

"I tell them right in the book, 'Who touches this touches a man.' "

"He actually touches two men, Walt, if he has but the gift to see it."

"What two men?"

"The man of the first 'Leaves of Grass,' Walt Whitman the Answerer, a cloudy prophet, a tortured giant. And the man of the later, shorter poems, the friend and comrade, the hopeful and serene."

"It is the same man, Fanny. The poet is growing older. There lies the explanation."

"If the poet is growing older, it seems to be as much by his own choice as through the passage of time."

"It is my own choice. My beard began to go gray ten years ago. My sister Mary wanted me to shave it. Shave it. Not I! Mary said to me, 'You're an odd one, Walt. Whereas everybody else seems to try all they can to keep young, you glory in the fact that you are already beginning to look venerable."

"I think I understand. It isn't the gray hair itself that appeals to you. It's the thought of growing into unity with life."

"Perhaps, Fanny, it's the thought of growing past passion into serenity. Mind you, I don't take back a single thing I have said about the imperative body, about sex and amativeness. That is fundamental. Yet there may come a time when it ceases to plague a man, when in comparison with other things it is not even important."

"You mean a mature man has no need of women?"

"A man may at length find himself possessed by a woman, and so completely possessed that what we call love becomes quite negligible in the sum."

"That sounds interesting. It just doesn't sound likely."

"Of course, love has its place still, though it no longer fills the room. And of course it demands a very special sort of woman to engross a man's every faculty. You yourself are that sort of woman, Fanny."

"I'm not even a legally free woman."

"That matters less than your difficulties have made you think it matters. But if you were free——"

"If I were free, I should know how to appreciate my freedom."

"You mean by that?"

"If this terrible strain were eased, and I had my child and my money, I could swing along very fast. I believe I could double the size of the *Free Inquirer*, and triple its influence."

"Is that your idea of the suitable thing to do with freedom?"

"It's the thing I should care most about doing under any circumstances."

"Then actually the present state of affairs serves you just as well."

"Perhaps it serves me better. If I were free, I might have no more sense or strength than any other woman. But as things are—"

"Yes, Fanny?"

"You always lift me out of my black moods. Let us go for a walk now, and see what life we can observe in the streets. I see more when you are along than I ever see alone. And if you have brought me a new poem, you may come in at my house and read it to me. I find you a great tonic, Walt."

"I suppose I ought to be grateful for that much."

XX

1860

RALPH WALDO EMERSON,
WALT WHITMAN

*Of a bright sharp February midday
two men are pacing up and down beneath the old elms of Beacon Street,
Boston.*

"Do you often come here to walk, Mr. Whitman?"

"Here or elsewhere. There are many possibilities
for a walk in Boston. Twice a day at least I stroll
about for an hour to get the dust of the printing-office
out of my lungs."

"Then I did not trespass on your time when I asked
you to meet me here."

"You are more than welcome to my time, Mr.
Emerson. I can never forget that you were my earliest
advocate and warm defender."

"It pricks my conscience sometimes that you may
think I have faltered in my advocacy."

"Why should I think that?"

"Because I have faltered, have allowed myself to
be influenced by a storm of censure with which I had
no sympathy. Let me clear my conscience by telling you.
When 'Leaves of Grass' first came out, in 1855, I
bought a copy with the idea of sending it to Carlyle."

[119]

"I could have given you a copy for that purpose. But perhaps you never sent it."

"After some hesitation, I did send it. But my manner of sending was inexcusable. For I wrote to tell him that he might like the book or he might not—"

"That could have gone without saying. You could guarantee no one's liking, least of all Carlyle's."

"But I added that if he did not like it, he might use the leaves to light his pipe."

"Carlyle might have done better than that with it, Mr. Emerson. Carlyle is unique. He has the keenest mind in Britain, and the fullest, best equipped. Only he has an ailing body. Dyspepsia is to be traced in every page, and now and then fills the page."

"You think his unbalanced health shows in his work?"

"It must show in every man's work, if it exists in his life. Behind the tally of genius and morals stands the stomach, and gives a casting vote."

"That was something of my own feeling, Whitman. 'Leaves of Grass' is a healthy book, and should benefit a man. Yet I think in my hesitation there was more than prejudice. I had, and have, a lingering doubt as to whether a book written so on impulse was exactly calculated to the capacity of the reader. I mean even the great reader. Even Carlyle."

"But Carlyle must have read 'Leaves of Grass.' I heard once on the subject from Conway. You remember Moncure Conway?"

"He is now abroad. I, too, hear sometimes from him."

"Conway wrote that he had mentioned me to Carlyle, and Carlyle said, 'No, no, don't quote that man! He's the fellow who thinks he must be a big man because he lives in a big country.'"

"I don't see how you can laugh at that, Whitman. I call it wretchedly unfair."

"It is unfair, of course. But behind its unfairness it shows a kind of understanding. I walk here under the elms on Beacon Street, and admire the bare boughs against the sky."

"They are very beautiful, aren't they? A delicate tracery, wild yet ordered."

"I admire them, and Boston which encloses them. Then I think of the great Western prairies, and the basin of the Mississippi, and it occurs to me that the child is already born who will see a hundred million people, the most powerful and advanced of the world, inhabiting this country of ours."

"A great thought, Whitman, so be it the hundred millions or any considerable fraction of them are men, not mere automatons or figures in the census."

"Wait! I am only approaching my thought. For grander than the fact itself it would be to have all those illimitable American areas fused in the alembic of a perfect poem, entirely Western, frank, and limitless, altogether our own poem, without a trace or taste of Europe's soil, without reminiscence in technical letter or in spirit."

"Doubtless, doubtless! Is that shaggy old man trying to attract your attention?"

"Oh, hello, Elephant! See you later, Elephant, or tomorrow if not today. Yes, that is Old Elephant, who used to be a bus driver in New York. His brother Young Elephant has succeeded him."

"I suppose that—er, 'Elephant' is a nickname?"

"Originally it was. But with men of that class, a nickname is the true name. Given at first for some peculiar quality, it gradually supersedes the more formal name in common use. Some of the bus drivers, George Storms or Pete Callahan, have names like another man's. But mostly they are Broadway Jack, Dressmaker, Balky Bill, Yellow Joe——"

"You have them catalogued."

"I will not pour out the catalogue on you. Let my catalogues stay in my books."

"Quite the contrary, Whitman. Let what will come up in the course of talk with a friend. Even if misunderstood it should give no offense. But what is to appear in a book should be scrutinized again and again."

"That is exactly my own policy, Mr. Emerson. In this third edition of 'Leaves of Grass' I am including many new poems. But also I have revised and rearranged all the old ones."

"Leaving out whatever might give offense to a public taste perhaps too squeamish?"

"Well, no. Leaving out not much of anything. The very poems to which you allude are essential to my scheme."

"Yet on the basis of those poems, Mr. Whitman, I have heard you quoted as an upholder of the doctrine of free love."

"If that is as far as your friends go in opposition to me, they are kinder than the run of my readers."

"You are surely not a believer in free love?"

"If a man believes in love at all——"

"Yes, Mr. Whitman?"

"What other kind of love is there?"

"I think I see your point. .Love must go where it chooses. Truly it must. But as a basis for society the so-called system of free love would be bad, very bad indeed."

"It might be. There is no doubt that marriage forms must change, and are even now changing. But in what way they are to change is not my concern. That change should be left to the women."

"To the women, Mr. Whitman? But they are the very ones whom marriage laws must protect. What will become of the foundations of society if our mothers are mothers for love rather than for some other reason?"

"Why, the mothers *are* the foundations of society. Mothers need no law."

"If that is the conclusion to be reached from your book, I for one should not quarrel with it. But I am afraid the average reader would draw no such conclusion. I am afraid you will be tangled up with the unfortunate heresy of free love."

"But according to you that has already occurred. Therefore, precautions against it would be useless. And to my own knowledge worse heresies than that have been charged against me."

"You seem to be aware of your position, Mr. Whitman. Then the point is, what are you going to do about it?"

"Do? Why, nothing."

"Nothing at all?"

"Nothing I could do now would mend matters."

"Ah, but it would! You have given your book no chance to be popularly seen or apprehended. If you cut out the bits that offend the censors, you would have a book that must go through editions, might go through many editions."

"Then you advise me to geld my book for the sake of editions and royalties?"

"Not so fast, please! Not so fast! I do indeed present the worldly argument. I want the book to sell. Yet I want it to sell not so much for your sake as for the sake of the buyers. You don't need the people so much as the people need you."

"If I cut it as you suggest, do you think there would be a book left?"

"Yes, Mr. Whitman, I do."

"But would there be as good a book left?"

"I did not say as good a book. But a good book. Yes, indeed, a very good book. Will you be patient with me if I try to take the matter up from the beginning?"

"If you can find where the beginning is, you are welcome to begin there."

"In the first place, an author owes a duty to the community. In your earlier editions, especially the second, are things which I should hesitate to discuss with you here and now. In spite of the boasted frankness of men with men, the mere mention of them would embarrass me. I venture to think it would also embarrass you. How, then, can such things be put into print and sown broadcast without the risk, indeed without the certainty, of misapprehension?"

"True. The mention of certain things is always misapprehended."

"If we were perfect beings dwelling in a perfect world, that would be different. Even if in the world as it is we could know perfectly what we are about, that would again be different. But, as we are situated, there may be a balance of reason against our endeavors. There is certainly a balance of power."

"Just what do you mean by that, Mr. Emerson?"

"Let us fall back on the crystallized wisdom of the proverb, 'Half a loaf is better than no bread.' 'Leaves of Grass' even without the—the sex poems would be better than denunciation or silence."

"I am still here, and able to do my day's work and eat my vittles. Yet I have endured both denunciation and silence."

"But why go on enduring them? Anyhow, what is the point of a book without readers? Unless a book is read it is like a stone dropped into a bottomless well. To put into a book what you know will drive readers away is to defeat your purpose in the beginning."

"I see perfectly what you mean. You marshal your arguments like an army corps in order, artillery, cavalry, infantry."

"You have followed my arguments?"

"Followed them perfectly."

"Then what have you to say in answer?"

"I can't answer them at all, Mr. Emerson."

"And what will you do in regard to them?"

"What will I do? There is only one thing for me to do. I can do nothing but adhere to my own theory and exemplify it."

"And your theory is what?"

"I want to get a complete human being into a book."

"Perhaps we aren't quite complete in Concord. But I thought it my duty to warn you. I'm sorry my words were useless."

"They were by no means useless. Up to now I have been touched with qualms."

"And now?"

"Now they have altogether gone from me."

"Perhaps I have done something for you, even if it was not what I wanted to do. Are you in a hurry, Mr. Whitman?"

"I am never in a hurry."

"Then let us go over to the American House and have a good dinner. I've worked up a splendid appetite as a result of my efforts. I am sorry if it is to be their sole result."

"It is not the sole result, Mr. Emerson. I much appreciate your friendly advice."

"And altogether refuse to take it?"

"Altogether."

"Let us call the matter settled, and say no more about it. I still believe that my contention is right. But I like you all the better, perhaps, for your refusal to compromise."

"It would be decenter to throw the book away than to mutilate it."

"It will be decentest of all to keep it. Doubtless in time even your difficult truths will prevail."

"I have all the time there is."

"You really feel that, don't you? How splendid is human dauntlessness, even in this Boston climate! And how I am going to enjoy that dinner!"

XXI

1861

PATSY DEE, WALT WHITMAN

*The Yellow Bird stage rattles down
Broadway, New York, on a spring
night. Perched beside the driver,
Walt Whitman is declaiming at the
top of his lungs the opening lines of
"Richard II." The driver, with his
attention divided between his horses
and possible fares, is an acquiescent if
not an attentive listener.*

" 'Old John of Gaunt, time-honored Lancaster,
Hast thou, according to thy oath and bond,
Brought hither Henry Hereford thy bold son,
Here to make good the boisterous late appeal,
Which then our leisure would not let us hear,
Against the Duke of Norfolk, Thomas Mowbray?'

"You see, Patsy, that is King Richard speaking. He
is allowed to begin his own play. That's about all the
fun he does have."

"Go on, Walt. What comes next?"

"Do you like it?"

"Well, I don't know what it's all about. But it
seems to kind of go in with all the rest of the racket."

"There's an air of excitement tonight, isn't there? The streets are so full of people, and all the gas-lamps going. It's as bright as day."

"People are waiting for the news from the South. They think General Beauregard means to fire on Fort Sumter."

"I can't believe he will go that far. The election set the South by the ears, and the Southern politicians have done their best to make a breach. All this business of secession is bad. I don't quite see how it is to be got over. But I hope not by war."

"I shouldn't wonder a bit if we had a war, and had it soon."

"But, Patsy, that would mean a war within our own country, and these States set one against another to destroy the Union! I can't believe it will come to that."

"Hope not, I'm sure. Do you want to drive a little, Walt?"

"The street is too full just now. I'll reach around and take the fares for you."

"Happen you had your fill of driving last winter?"

"Perhaps I did drive more than usual last winter. Did you think you saw me driving oftener?"

"My thinking hadn't nothing to do with it. I know you drove George Storms' stage all the time he was laid up with a broken leg."

"George promised me he wouldn't say anything about that."

"He didn't. Dr. Roosa told me in the Broadway hospital, when I went there to get something done about my lame hand."

"George Storms couldn't afford to lose his job. He

has a wife and family. He isn't a free bird like you and me."

"He'd have lost it all right if it hadn't been for you."

"I was glad of the experience, Patsy. But Dr. Roosa shouldn't have given me away."

"He likes you. Says when the fellows are in the hospital after an accident, nothing does them so much good as a visit from you. Says you do him good too. A glass of beer with you after hours makes up for all he has to put up with during the day."

"He's a valuable and important man. You know he has a queer name, St. James or St. John. If a really bad accident is brought into the hospital, or if something happens that nobody else knows what to do about, you hear them begin to holler, 'Where's the saint?'"

"Yes, he's a good man. Likes his beer too, after hours."

"Hello, Balky! What's the matter with you, Patsy, that you don't greet your sister stage? The Red Bird just passed us going up Broadway."

"I drive my own stage, and that's enough for me to attend to."

"You had an eye for that fare too, didn't you? Your own business keeps you busy."

"I say, Walt, if a war does come, they'll be wanting a lot of soldiers. The single men will go first. Think you'll go?"

"You mean take a musket and shoot my Southern friends because I happen to disagree with them on some points of public policy. I think I'll not do anything of the kind."

"But war is war, Walt. Once we're in it, what can we do but go ahead and fight?"

"All war is butchery, but a war within a country is unthinkable butchery. It is brother against brother. But I cannot seriously believe we shall reach quite such a point of madness."

"Sometimes you talk like a blooming Quaker. You wear a hat like a Quaker's too. You don't belong to them, do you?"

"When I was a young man I thought seriously of joining them. But no, I don't belong to the Quakers nor to any one else. To belong to myself, and to myself alone, has become my idea and ideal."

"You talk awful hifalutin sometimes, Walt. But this was a good pair of gloves you give me last fall without any talk at all. I wore 'em all winter, and you see they're still good. It's gettin' too warm for 'em now. I'll put 'em away soon and save 'em till fall."

"The hifalutin talk has more to do with the gloves than you suspect. Last fall I bought gloves for you and all my special friends among the drivers out of the profits from my poems."

"My God, Walt, I never think about your poems! You're a good sort if you do claim to be a poet."

"It isn't just a claim, Patsy. People buy my poems."

"But not many people, do they?"

"A good many this time. I'm thankful to say some thousands of people. A kindly and intelligent publisher in Boston is beginning to pull out of a bad hole because he has an interest in my poems."

"You say people really pay good money just for poems?"

"They do. Walt Whitman, forty-two years old next

month, self-constituted poet of democracy and the common man, interpreter to themselves of these States, is at last nearing the top rung of the ladder. If the ladder will but hold!"

"So you're makin' money same as if you worked for it, Walt?"

"Just the same."

"Well, if that don't beat all! Reach around and get that fare, will you? Saves me makin' change."

"Here it is."

"You may as well go on now about old John of Gaunt. If you shout loud enough I can hear you. Anyhow, it's a nice cheerful noise, and keeps a fellow from feelin' lonesome up here on the box."

"But that's poetry too, Patsy."

"I know. But I don't have to pay nothin' for it."

"Oh, very well then, so long as it's worth what it comes to! I'll begin back at the beginning.

" 'Old John of Gaunt, time-honored Lancaster—'

I say, Patsy, I believe the papers have another extra out."

"They do that all the time nowadays. They know they can sell 'em."

"But people are grabbing the papers and shouting to each other. You don't suppose that fire-eater Beauregard has actually done what he threatened?"

"Can't say, I'm sure. Time enough for me to find out when I go off duty."

"But look at the crowd going into Niblo's Hotel! Let me down here. I can find out in Niblo's just what the news is."

"Pshaw, Walt! I was countin' on your company."

"Wait right here, then, and I'll come back."

"It's against the rules to hold the stage so long."

"Then I won't get down. Just slow up a little. There must be some one we can shout down to. Yes, I see a man I know. Hello there, O'Brien! What's the cause of all the excitement? What's the news?"

"What makes you look so funny, Walt? You've fair turned green."

"Didn't you hear what that man said?"

"He said they'd fired on Fort Sumter. But wasn't that just what you expected?"

"Not what I expected. Not what I can even believe. The gas-lamps burning just as usual. You and I on the box, and the off horse twitching his ear at us. Yet Fort Sumter has been fired on!"

"Yep. That means war. Reach back and take that fare, will you, Walt? Means war, all right. And time we had it, too, if you're askin' me."

XXII

1862

LOUISA VAN VELSOR WHITMAN, WALT WHITMAN

*Late on a December day the widow
Whitman sits in her cozy, immaculate
kitchen. She is knitting in the silence
which befits the families of authors.
Established at the kitchen table, her
gray-bearded son has been covering a
stray sheet of wrapping-paper and
the backs of several old envelopes
with his legible, deliberate writing.
Presently he reads over what he has
written and lays it aside.*

"That's enough writing for today, Mother. Now
we can talk."

"I'm listening, Walt. What have you to say?"

"Writing is hungry work. What about a cup of tea
and some pancakes?"

"We will have supper as soon as Jeff gets home."

"Supper is a kindly meal, the pleasantest of the day.
Nowadays it has become an event I look forward to,
with sister Mat and the little girl at the table, and
Louisa sitting at the head. But I wouldn't mind a cup
of tea just with Louisa. She looks so Velsorish in her

white cap, and the kitchen is so cozy and comfortable."

"I could wish George had half as good."

"Why, so could I, Mother. But George was never a man to sit down and be cozy."

"It's little chance he has of coziness these days."

"Your mind must run on George. You can't help that. But don't get the idea that he's worse off than he is. George has none of the Quaker in him. He's in his element in the army. You can tell that by the way he has won promotion."

"George has done well in the army."

"You say that dryly, madam. Has any one been bothering you because your other son is not in the army?"

"Which son? Jeff or Andrew?"

"Neither, Madam Innocent. Jeff is a family man now, and poor Andrew a sick one. Not that I believe Andrew's throat is so bad as we sometimes fear. We shall have him well again one of these days."

"I'm sure I hope so."

"But until his throat is well, Andrew must stay at home. Where would a soldier be without a voice? It was Walt I was speaking of, however. Has some one been saying things to you because I'm not in the army?"

"Thee knows people do talk about that sometimes, Walt."

"Don't be too meek when they do. There's a good deal to be said for my letting the army alone. In the first place, I should make a very poor soldier. I am too old, too large, too slow."

"Aye, thee is slow enough, in all conscience."

"Then, too, I have a dread of fighting. Not only of

being shot at, but of being led out and told that I must shoot somebody."

"Yet thee voted for Mr. Lincoln, Walt, and even spoke during the campaign."

"When I must have seen that certain things would lead to war? Right you are. But you see I approve of the war. It's just of fighting that I don't approve."

"Walt, does thee not sometimes—just sometimes, Walt—look for differences where there are none?"

"Capital, Louisa, capital! You never use the Quaker 'thee' unless you want to score. You have scored this time."

"Thee likes war, but thee doesn't like to fight."

"And you see no difference there?"

"The truth is, Walt, that thee likes words."

"Exactly. I've been trying to get the war down in words. I want to make a book that shall include the war as 'Leaves of Grass' included the man. I think I shall call the new book 'Drum Taps.'"

"I don't know much about thy poetry, Walt. Thee knows that."

"Perhaps you agree with some of the critics that it isn't poetry at all?"

"I'd hardly like to say that. I've been looking lately into Mr. Longfellow's 'Hiawatha.' If that is poetry, 'Leaves of Grass' may be."

"I suppose it bothers you just as it did George. George thinks I have talent, but don't make the proper use of it. The only time he ever talked to me about my book, he ended by shouting at me that I was as stubborn as hell."

"George shouldn't use such language. But don't you think your poems would sell better if you made them

[135]

look just a little better? All those scraps of paper seem
so untidy."

"I should copy them if they were poems. But I've
been prosing today. This is another of the 'Brooklyn-
iana' articles for the *Standard*."

"Then you will get money for this, Walt?"

"For this, and for as many others as I may care to
write. I've done twenty-five articles so far, and the
series has been very popular."

"It's nice to get money for them. I don't quite see,
though, why people want to pay money to read about
old buildings and old Mr. Hartshorne the printer and
that old story about how Lafayette picked thee up and
kissed thee when thee was a little boy."

"People do like to read about those very things."

"If you can get money for such old stories, Walt,
there is no reason why you should not always have
money."

"If I can keep up my own interest I shall be all right.
But I'm beginning to tire of the history and antiquities
of Brooklyn."

"Ay, Walt, when things begin to go smoothly with
thee, thee always begins to get tired."

"I might feel differently about it if you fed me
oftener. Come, Louisa, let me have a cup of tea. Bread
and butter will do nicely, if you don't care to make
pancakes."

"I will put on the tea-kettle, Walt. Wasn't that a
knock at the door? See who it is."

"It's a telegram for you, Mother."

"A telegram? That means the army—George."

"Do you want me to open it?"

"Open it, Walt. He must be—killed."

"Wait a moment until I see. Come, this isn't so bad. He has been wounded at the battle of Fredericksburg. But only wounded, Mother. He's alive, as alive as I am."

"But wounded, my boy George! And down there among strangers, where I can't look to him!"

"Yes. We can't have him left alone when he's in need of help. Mother, how would it be if I went down and found him?"

"You mean if you went down to the battle-field, Walt? But they wouldn't let you."

"I may need a pass or something. But I can get that in Washington. I have friends now in Washington. William O'Connor has gone there from Boston, and poor Eldridge, who was my publisher until the war ruined him."

"You will need things, Walt, money, baggage. But perhaps you can start tomorrow."

"I have some money by me, fifty dollars or a little more. That will do nicely. I can get the first train for Washington."

"But you aren't taking even a carpet-bag. And why are you gathering up those scraps of paper?"

"I must leave them at the *Standard* office on my way to the station. I can buy whatever I need in Washington."

"I'm sure if you ever reach him, Walt, you can help and comfort poor George. But I hate having you start off like this."

"You're surprised at my going so quickly. So am I. But I have a feeling that George needs me. Kiss Jeff's little girl for me. And for yourself this, and this."

"I wish you would at least take a carpet-bag."

"You are not to worry about me, Mother. Only there is one thing you can see to for me, if you will."

"Yes, Walt?"

"Upstairs I have left a little manuscript book that says 'Drum Taps' on the cover. Will you save it for me? I shouldn't like anything to happen to that."

"Is that all?"

"No. There's a copy of 'Leaves of Grass' in blue paper, and some manuscript tied up in loose spotted paper covers. I'd take them with me if I could. But if you'll just see that they come to no harm——"

"George's wound must be bad, Walt, or they wouldn't have sent us a telegram."

"I will send you word, Mother. You shall hear just as soon as possible."

XXIII

1863

SENATOR PRESTON KING,
WALT WHITMAN

On a January day, in the "parlor chambers" of the United States Senate, Senator Preston King of New York is receiving an applicant for office. The applicant is making a mental note of the Senator: "as fat as a hogshead, with great hanging chops." But not all fat men are good-natured; and the Senator has more applications than he can count, let alone fill.

"Now, just what is it you want? Tell me as briefly as possible. I'm a busy man."

"I want a clerkship in one of the departments."

"What department?"

"Any department."

"What kind of clerkship?"

"Any kind of clerkship. I can manage whatever work is wanted."

"Think well of your own ability, don't you?"

"I have noticed that people can usually do what they are set down to do. I thought if you knew of a vacancy you might arrange to shove me in."

[139]

"You thought I might shove you in? How could I? Or why should I? How do I know but you are a Secessionist? You look for all the world like an old Southern planter—a regular Carolina or Virginia planter."

"See here, Senator King, there seems to be some mistake. I'm a Brooklyn newspaper man. I've just furnished to the Brooklyn *Standard* a series of articles describing Brooklyn from the earliest days."

"You may have or you may not. I don't know."

"But hasn't Charles Sumner prepared the way for me? He was supposed to write you a letter."

"Supposed to, was he? Well, he didn't. I haven't heard a word from him."

"Then we must get along without Sumner. Let me tell you why I want this clerkship. I was at home in Brooklyn in December when I got a telegram calling me down to the field at Fredericksburg. My brother, who is a captain in a Brooklyn regiment, had been wounded."

"What's that got to do with your hunting a clerkship?"

"I started South at once in search of my brother. When I passed through Washington I had my pocket picked, and was left penniless. But I found an old friend in Washington, and managed to borrow enough money to take me on. At Fredericksburg I found my brother. He had been shot in the cheek, but not badly. He was back at the head of his company. But there were others not so fortunate. Senator King, have you ever been in a field hospital?"

"No, I haven't. What would I want in a field hospital?"

"What would anybody want there who could stay

away? But I was there, and I went into a field hospital. It was a large brick mansion on the banks of the Rappahannock immediately opposite Fredericksburg. It is used as a hospital right along, and receives only the worst cases. Outdoors at the foot of a tree, within ten yards of the front of the house, I saw a heap of amputated limbs, feet, legs, arms, hands. It would make a load for a one-horse cart."

"Faugh! How disgusting!"

"I went into that hospital. I saw men badly wounded, some frightfully. Some of them were dying. They all lay there in their old clothes, unclean and bloody."

"That's war. There's nothing we can do about it."

"I thought perhaps there was something I could do about it. That very first day I wrote a few letters home for soldiers. Some of them could not write. Some were too sick and weak. Then for ten days I went about among the regimental and division hospitals. They were not even old houses. They were tents, not equipped with cots, seldom with even a mattress on the ground. In many of them water was standing."

"I suppose like every one else you blame the Government. But the Government has been handicapped, terribly handicapped."

"New Year's Day I came up to Washington on the steamer. I had been lucky in finding my brother not so badly off as I feared. But there were plenty of other people's brothers who were worse off. Since I reached Washington I've been going to some hospital or other every day. Often at one time there are as many as fifty thousand wounded or sick in Washington."

"Does it do any good if you walk about and look at them?"

"It would do good, if I did only that. Most of these wounded soldiers are mere boys. They are desperately homesick and lonely, grateful if a man even calls them by name and stops to talk to them. But there are many little comforts that can be given them, little services too."

"What sort of services?"

"I read to some of them, give reading matter to others. I write letters for them, many, many letters. To those who are well enough to write their own letters I give stationery and stamps. Many of them come up here without a cent in their pockets, and nothing does them so much good as a little money. I give away a lot of money, in sums of from fifteen to thirty cents. Others want some small article that I can get for them, a comb, a toothbrush, a clean shirt. I make a note of all such wants, and try to supply them on my next visit."

"That's admirable, so far as it goes. But you said yourself there are fifty thousand wounded in Washington. What good can one man do among so many cases?"

"The hospitals could use a hundred such workers. But I make myself go farther than you might expect. Sometimes I go rapidly through a whole ward, giving each man some small present, an orange, a sweet cracker, a spoonful of jelly. After that I sit down with the worst cases. Already once or twice the doctors have told me that my presence made all the difference. It roused some soldier from his lethargy and homesickness, made him want to get well."

"You speak of the doctors. How do the doctors take your interference?"

"They are commonly very kind to me. Most of our army surgeons are noble men and skilful. They, too, feel how inadequate are their efforts in the face of all that is to be done."

"What you tell me is really very interesting, Mr.——"

"Whitman."

"Mr. Whitman. It's evident that there is negligence somewhere. Congress appropriates money enough to buy two mattresses apiece for every soldier under arms, and then our wounded lie on the ground in mud-puddles. There seems to be something wrong with our system."

"All systems rest on men."

"Quite true. There may be something wrong with the men. A mob of job hunters aren't much good when it comes to getting things done."

"I came here as a job hunter, Senator King."

"So you did, so you did. How have you been living since you came to Washington?"

"I've written letters to the Brooklyn and New York papers. Then my friend Major Hapgood has given me some copying to do. He is the paymaster, and allows me a desk in his office for my writing. But he has no permanent position for me."

"If this matter of bread and butter was taken care of, you could do better for the soldiers in the hospitals?"

"I should have a freer mind, Senator, as well as a little more money."

"We'll have to see what we can do for you."

"That was what I hoped for."

"Don't build too much on any politician's promise, Mr. Whitman. You saw what Sumner's was good for. But sit down a minute and I will write you a letter to Secretary Chase. And maybe one to General Meigs, of the Quartermaster's Department. That's where all the mattresses go that are never heard of afterward."

"Shall I sit down here, Senator?"

"Anywhere, anywhere you like. Do you realize how long you've kept me standing?"

XXIV

1863

FRANK DARNELL, WALT WHITMAN

The second story of the Patent Office in Washington is now in use as an army hospital. It is a large, lofty room containing rank after rank of high glass cases filled with models of inventions. Between the ranks of cases, in the wide center aisle and around the gallery are crowded cots, each cot bearing a sick or wounded soldier. A large ruddy civilian, freshly bathed and dressed in clean plain gray clothes, is making the rounds with a full haversack. He pauses at each bed, leaves a small gift, asks whether there is anything a soldier especially needs, and writes down requests. When he comes to Darnell's cot he pauses, puts his notebook away, and sits down.

"May I sit here a minute after my rounds?"

"Guess so."

"I come through the wards sometimes to see if there is anything the soldiers want. I have good friends who help me get those things. Is there anything we can get for you?"

"There's nothing I want except to get out of here."

"You haven't been here long, have you? I don't remember seeing you before."

"I've been here only four days. Seems like four hundred! You're the first human being that has spoke to me since I come in here. I don't count doctors and nurses. They ain't human."

"They are very busy. Especially after a battle they are sadly overworked."

"Trying to say a good word for them, ain't you? They need it. There was a parson fellow in here yesterday wanting to pray with me. Pray with me! A secesh done better than that for me."

"A secesh? Tell me about him. What was his name?"

"Don't know his name. Never will know it. 'Twas after I was wounded at Fredericksburg."

"Was he a rebel soldier?"

"Didn't seem to be a soldier. But he talked funny, like all them Southerners."

"Did he find you lying on the field?"

"He had time enough to find me. I got it in the leg and in the side on Saturday. Then I laid for two days and nights just where I fell."

"But what were the stretcher bearers doing? Didn't any one from the Union lines try to move you to safety?"

"They couldn't come anywhere near me. I was between the city and the batteries. The worst of it was, I was laying with my head downhill and couldn't move

to help myself. And every time a secesh come near I
was scared to death. I'd heard stories of what they
done to the wounded."

"But none of them hurt you?"

"Two rebel soldiers had come by and talked rough,
but they didn't abuse me. I tell you I kept mighty quiet
while they was near. Then the second day this fellow
come up and spoke to me. He was a middle-aged man,
and seemed to be working among the wounded."

"He spoke kindly, tried to help you?"

"He did help me. He bound up my wounds, and
gave me a drink of whisky and a couple of biscuits."

"Did he move you so that you no longer lay with
your head downhill?"

"I asked him to, but he was afraid to try on account
of starting my wounds bleeding. But my head felt
better after he'd talked to me. He even asked if I could
relish a little bit of cooked beef."

"And after that our own men brought you in?"

"They might better of left me. The secesh was a
man. There's one rebel that's going to Heaven. But
our fellows yanked me into what they called a hospital. There they let me lay on a cot made of poles
and boughs, with water standing in the tent. My
wounds gangrened. Then when they thought I was
going to die they brought me up to Washington. Our
boys hate being brought up to Washington. They think
then they sure will die."

"Have you written home since you were wounded?"

"I never wrote home much. I can't write very good.
Now I don't want to worry them telling how bad I'm
hurt."

"But they would be glad to know you are safe in the hospital. That at least is something. So many men are reported missing."

"Suppose my mother feels that way about it. She's getting old. I was her youngest."

"Would you like it if I wrote a letter for you?"

" 'Twould be a load off Mother's mind, perhaps. But why should you bother? You don't even know me."

"I think I do, now. Just give me your mother's name and address, and I'll put it right on this envelope so you can see me do it. Then tonight after I get home I'll write the letter."

"Mrs. Susie Darnell, Kent's Crossing, Wisconsin. You're not a Wisconsin man yourself, are you?"

"No, New York. My own mother lives in Brooklyn."

"I just thought you might be from the West. You look so big and bearded. Not like them shiny shaved dudes of doctors."

"More like a buffalo right off the prairie, don't I? There, you see the envelope is done."

"It looks kind of good to see Mother's name in writing. Almost like seeing her for a minute. You're not going now?"

"Not if you want me to stay. I'm in no hurry."

"I suppose it's foolish, but the pain in my side seems better when you sit there and talk to me. And I'd rather look at you than at them blasted cases full of steam-engines that don't run. Sometimes along after midnight they get to look like coffins. Rows and rows of shiny damned coffins."

"It makes a difference what a man looks at, doesn't

it? When you get back the use of your legs you can choose what you will look at."

"'D' know as it makes much difference."

"It does to me. I like to roam about and look at things. Last night when I left the hospital I went to the Capitol building."

"What for?"

"Just to wander about and see it when it was lighted up. It's very brilliant of an evening with all the gas-lamps going. I spent an hour or more in the long rich corridors under the Senate. They were brightly lighted like the rest, but there were not many people about. Just now and then a flitting figure in the distance."

"That's kind of nice to think about. They brought me straight up here from the wharf. I didn't know there was anything in Washington but wounded men and hospitals."

"There's the President's house, for one thing. The White House, they call it."

"Is it really all white?"

"All white. All built of stone."

"I s'pose you've seen it many times?"

"It is a noble sight at any time. But I like it best under a full moon, and seen between the green branches of trees in full leaf."

"Sounds purty, like something in a book."

"It is like something in the finest kind of book."

"But do they let you wander around and look at everything? How do they know you ain't a rebel? I sh'd think there might be rebels even in Washington."

"There are sentries everywhere, in their blue over-coats and peaked caps. They look at me sharply, but they never try to stop me. They walk back and forth, back and forth. Some of them walk all night. They must get very sleepy."

"Huh! You don't know how sleepy, if you've never done sentry go. The thought of it makes this old cot comfortable."

"You are getting sleepy yourself, aren't you?"

"Just dozy. You ain't going?"

"I shall be back tomorrow, to let you know I have sent that letter to your mother."

"If you want to write to her I mustn't keep you. But you'll sure be back tomorrow?"

"Sure will."

"That will give me something to think about if I wake up in the night. I won't look at those damn coffins of cases."

"Think of the sentries walking all night while you lie here snug and warm."

"Yes. And I'll think of them just looking at you, and letting you go on."

XXV

1863

ALEXANDER VAN RENSSELAER, PRESIDENT LINCOLN

*Mr. Van Rensselaer, who has come
as the bearer of one of the urgent
messages of these urgent times,
learns that the President is not in the
White House. Just as he is leaving,
however, he encounters the returning
Executive near the door of the East
Room.*

"Mr. Lincoln, may I stop you for a moment? I was
asked to bring a certain matter to your attention."

"Is it pressing?"

"Mr. Hay said you would have to deal with it yourself. He couldn't."

"If Hay thinks I ought to atend to it, let me have
it."

"It's this letter which my Congressman wished
brought directly to your attention. Sometimes in the
ordinary course of business these things get over-
looked."

"Step in here with me while I read it, and I can let
you have an answer. There is still light enough in the
East Room to read by."

[151]

"It won't take you long."

"No. More of the same, I see. Row in the Sanitary Commission this time. Tell your Congressman I'll do what I can about it."

"Thank you, Mr. President. It's a shame to waylay you with business during the little time you might have to yourself."

"Time to myself? I don't know what that means. Let me be just, though. Every day or two I have a few minutes to stand and look out of these windows. Usually it happens about this same hour."

"You enjoy the view, Mr. President?"

"Not the view strictly speaking. But the sight of the people who pass and look up at the White House."

"I suppose everybody in America passes these windows sooner or later."

"The same people seem to pass every day."

"Perhaps they look so much alike as to be hardly distinguishable."

"That may be it. There is one fellow, though, who has roused my curiosity. He comes by here almost every day, and even Hay doesn't know who he is. Yet it's Hay's job to know everybody."

"What does he look like?"

"He's a big man, and always walks at about the same rate, neither hurrying nor dragging. He has a gray beard, not very much trimmed. It blows in the wind. He wears a wide-brimmed hat thrust to the back of his head, and hands thrust in the side pockets of his ulster."

"That sounds as if it might be—"

"Never mind my poor description. Here he comes

now. That man in gray, looking at everybody and speaking to almost everybody."

"It's the man I thought it must be, Mr. President. He's quite a well-known figure in Washington. He is an old newspaper man. He visits the army hospitals very often and works among the wounded."

"Have I ever heard of him?"

"You may have. His name is Walt Whitman."

"Walt Whitman, eh? Is he a Westerner?"

"No. He comes originally from Brooklyn."

"And he goes around and talks to the wounded?"

"That isn't such a waste of time as you might think, Mr. President. The doctors say he has a wonderful influence over sick people. I have heard him criticized for not taking a more active part in the war. But I think he does a work that no one else could do. Or at any rate not so well as he does it."

"And I was thinking—"

"Yes, Mr. President?"

"Well, *he* looks like a MAN."

XXVI

1864

MRS. TURNER ASHBY, WALT WHITMAN

In February of 1864 there has been more fighting near Culpepper, Virginia. A Confederate general's widow who has Northern officers quartered in her fine old family mansion falls into talk with a civilian whose presence so near the front is not quite accounted for.

"That was an excellent supper, Mrs. Ashby."

"It was better at least than last night's."

"Let us hope that the improvement continues, and we have a quieter night all through."

"You were roused by the disturbance in the night?"

"I had been advised not to go to sleep, as we might have to move at any hour. We have already taken and lost Culpepper three or four times."

"My count would be five or six."

"The bed in my room looked very good, and I was very sleepy. I lay down and slept sweetly and freshly until about three o'clock. Then I heard a disturbance that did not die down. I dressed and came outdoors. It was only some troops returning from the extreme

front. But very picturesque they looked in the half
light as they came marching past like columns of
shadows."

"You would have lost your taste for the spectacle
if you had seen it as many times as I have."

"You have stayed here in your old home since the
beginning of the war, Mrs. Ashby?"

"Since the beginning of the war."

"But shall you stay on now that the fighting seems
to concentrate about here?"

"I shall stay as long as I can hold out. I hope I may
hold out to the end."

"But it must be extremely unpleasant for a woman
like you, a traveled, educated woman, to live between
the lines of moving armies. Unpleasant if not actually
dangerous."

"It is not so dangerous as you might suppose, but
it is worse than unpleasant. It is humiliating. The place
has not been planted for three years, and would
scarcely yield now if we could plant it. I live on chance
and charity."

"But isn't there somewhere you could go, and escape
these shifts and pinches?"

"I would go somewhere, anywhere, if I were free
to do so. But I have children."

"Couldn't you take them with you?"

"It isn't that. I hold the plantation on their account.
Bad as it looks, it is still a fine property in comparison
with the plantations their owners have deserted."

"Your children should be proud of their mother."

"I do not wish them to be ashamed of her. Their
father was a brave man."

"You say 'was'?"

"He fell in battle."

"I beg your pardon, Mrs. Ashby. I should have guessed."

"Don't apologize. I like to talk of him sometimes. We had happy years together. I was not unprepared for his death. Our Confederate army has lost many generals. Yet there was one thing which hurt me at the time and still rankles. . . . But I don't know why I am telling you all this. It can't interest you."

"It does interest me. And surely it will do you good to speak to some one of your troubles. Toward most of the world you show an unmoved front."

"I was only going to say that I felt terribly, felt until I was ashamed of it, my inability to put on mourning when word came of my husband's death. I have had no new clothes since the beginning of the war, and my one black dress wore to holes long ago."

"I do not think it strange that a broken heart misses the simple refinements of life. I have seen a soldier who was a hero under the surgeon's knife. Later I have heard that same soldier cry out loud because his hair was tangled and he had no comb."

"Have you seen much of that side of the war?"

"I have seen that side almost exclusively. I am down near the front now to see a little of another. But for more than a year I have been walking the wards in the army hospitals. I have seen a great deal of the suffering of war, and very little of the glory."

"Glory? There is no glory in war. The glory of war is a lie by which men cheat themselves. There is heroism of a sort on both sides. I myself have seen it. But there is no glory. Never any glory."

"You do not cheat yourself with a lie, Mrs. Ashby. Yet you go on."

"I feel that I have no choice in the matter. But you, sir—you are not officially attached to the army. Couldn't you get away?"

"I could. Often I promise myself that I will. My services to the soldiers are only a drop in the bucket, yet they exhaust my own life. But still—"

"There is always a 'but'?"

"Just recently my ministrations were interrupted for a time. One day I helped a surgeon who was operating on a gangrened limb. I do such things sometimes, because the patient asks me to. The knife slipped and cut my hand."

"Did the poison make you ill?"

"My arm swelled painfully, and became quite useless. For days I was forced to keep my room. The doctors thought my life was in danger. But my own worst trouble was just the fear that I might be forced to quit, to leave the ghastly sights and sounds of the hospital, and go quietly home, where I dream every night that I am."

"Human nature is like that, I'm afraid. We'd like to give in, but somehow we don't."

"We can't. That's it. We can't."

"You say your work lies among the hospitals. Does that mean you will be in this neighborhood for some time? There are plenty of hospitals within driving distance of Culpepper. Lately I fear they are never empty."

"Tomorrow I begin by doubling back on my tracks. The first day that I was in this neighborhood I found a small hospital of teamsters entirely without reading matter. I left with them all I had. It was a fair supply, thanks to the kindness of friends in the North. But I must collect it now and take it on. There are other such places. Each must have its turn."

"A hospital where there is nothing to read is too desolate to be endured. If you take back what you have given your teamsters, you must replace it with something else."

"But where am I to get more reading matter? I have had no fresh supplies from the North."

"Take a stale supply from the South, then. Come across the hall with me. I have nothing newer than 1860, of course. But the Ashbys were all readers. I will give you more books than you can carry."

"But the Ashby family books should be saved for your children."

"Suppose some day one of my children lay in the insufferable tedium of a hospital, with nothing to read?"

"You are a generous woman, Mrs. Ashby."

"Hold out your arms, and collect the books as I take them down. I suppose you have an accurate idea of what soldiers like?"

"They like almost anything these days. But, Mrs. Ashby,—"

"Yes?"

"Do you realize that the men these books are going to are Yankee teamsters?"

"God made them Yankees, sir. And perhaps they like this war no better than I do."

XXVII

1864

GEORGE WHITMAN, WALT WHITMAN

Burnside's corps is passing through Washington on its way to join the Army of the Potomac for the spring offensive of 1864. Captain George Whitman marches at the head of his company of the 51st New York. In Fourteenth Street a large gray-bearded man detaches himself from the watching crowd and falls into step beside Captain Whitman.

"Hello, George!"

"Hello, Walt! Where did you come from?"

"I've been waiting for you to pass. Thought I'd go a piece with you."

"I didn't expect to see you. We're not making any stop in Washington."

"I heard you wouldn't. So I've been waiting three hours for your regiment to come along."

"Three hours! You're a patient animal, Walt. I wouldn't wait three hours for God Almighty."

"A man learns patience in Washington. I've been waiting over a year for a Government clerkship. I've had plenty of promises, but so far nothing has come of them."

"Waiting seems to agree with you. You look pretty

much the same. Let's see, it's quite a while since I've seen you, isn't it?"

"I haven't seen you since you were wounded at Fredericksburg, and I came down to look for you."

"It was a mistake that you were sent for. My wound didn't amount to anything."

"It was more important for me than for you, George. You see, I've never gone back."

"You stay on in Washington, just so that you can go among the wounded in the hospitals? It seems like a queer taste."

"It is a queer taste. But I fancy I do them some good."

"I suppose it all helps in the long run."

"Sometimes, George, I think it is selfish of me to stick to my hospital work. There is Mother in Brooklyn growing old in poverty, and brother Andrew dying of his throat trouble, and Jesse falling off until he's not much better than poor Ed."

"I send Mother money when I can. But our pay is always behind, and of course I've my own family to care for. It would be more to the point if you went back to Brooklyn and went to work. Do you ever think of doing that?"

"Do I ever think of it! I dream nights of quiet comfortable dinners in Mother's kitchen, and taking little Mannahatta up to Fort Greene. I hope she isn't forgetting her Uncle Walt."

"If you really want to go back, nobody is stopping you."

"Hundreds are stopping me. If you could see the weary heads turn on pillows when I enter a ward! One boy wants a letter written home. Another wants a comb, a third some postage stamps. A group of half a dozen will gather for me to read to them. And some, the sickest ones, just want me to sit down beside them and stay."

"I suppose they take to you, Walt, because you're so hearty yourself."

"Like enough."

"But you haven't been so hearty all along, have you? Mother's letters said something about your being cut by a surgeon's knife."

"That was last summer. My hand is all healed."

"The cut may have healed. But those things sometimes stay in a man's system."

"I've nothing poisonous in my system except what you and Jeff used to call 'Walt's cussedness.' That and a book of poems which I can't get time to finish."

"I thought you published your book of poems before the war."

"I did, though I keep on adding to it and changing it. This is another book. 'Drum Taps,' I've called it."

"It's about the war, Walt?"

"It is. One way and another I've written a good deal about the war. I write letters back to the New York and Brooklyn papers. It brings me a bit of money, and keeps the people at home better in touch with their boys in the army. But the other day a fellow pitched into me in print for writing about the war instead of going to it. A fellow by the name of Higginson. It seems he went to war himself, though he's a parson by trade."

"He might a good deal better have stayed a parson."

"Do you know something about him, George?"

"Know all about him. He's quite well known, on account of the cuss words that follow him around."

"What he said bothered me, though. You can be frank with your old brother. Tell me, do you think I ought to have gone for a soldier?"

"You a soldier? Good God, no!"

"Spoken like a man. If you'd been more polite about it, I might have thought you were trying to spare my feelings."

"You're a little too womanish for a soldier, Walt. And you're a good deal too slow. You're doing pretty well for you to know that there is a war."

"Have your little joke. I know you like your old brother just the same. Look, the President is standing with General Burnside to see the troops go by."

"Where? Where?"

"On that balcony at our right. We are just passing them."

"That vexes me. I should have liked to salute the President."

"You can still salute him by turning a little."

"Well, I'm not going to turn. Not even a little."

"Spoken like a Whitman. It's too late now. We're past. Never mind, George. When the war is over you'll come back to Washington to be mustered out. Then you'll have plenty of chance to see the President and salute him."

"When the war is over—if it ever is. This is my second enlistment."

"I realized that when I stood waiting for you. This is an army of veterans, very different from those shows of soldiers I used to see in Brooklyn and New York, or on Fort Greene. These men of Burnside's corps are sunburnt and shaggy, with worn clothes and thin bundles. Nothing is neat about them except their muskets. But the muskets are clean and bright as silver."

"You notice everything, don't you? You were always a great one for a show, Walt."

"There's one show I'd be glad to miss. I mean the long trains of wounded coming up from the South, the boatloads of wounded landed at Aquia dock."

"So long as they keep on coming you'll keep on watching 'em."

"Mother likes to hear about the poor fellows. I tell Mother everything I see, and I write to her often. She likes to get letters from her sons."

"I write her myself when I can. But I dare say she'd rather hear from you. She thinks a sight of you."

"I don't think any more of Mother than you do, George. But I tell her about it."

"That's all right, if you can tell things."

"Have you any message you want to send by me?"

"No special message. Can't think of a thing."

"Then I believe I'll swing out of the procession at this next corner."

"You're anxious not to miss the rest of the show, I suppose. Go ahead."

"Sure you haven't any word to send to Mother and the rest?"

"No special word. Go along to the curb if you can make your way through the crowd. Then take off your hat as we pass. I'd like just one more sight of your wild gray head. A comb would get lost in that thatch, wouldn't it?"

"I'm going to trim it up like a dude's when you

catch Lee. Is that a colored regiment following yours? How do you find the colored troops behave?"

"Behave same as any others. There ought to be a colored regiment along some time if you watch for it."

"Then I'll watch."

"That's right. Don't miss anything, Walt. Not anything!"

XXVIII

1865

BARRETT SLOANE, WALT WHITMAN

A summer night in the Armory Square hospital, Washington. Most of the beds are now vacant, and the ward is dimly lighted. At the end farthest from the door Walt Whitman is sitting at the bedside of a young man who lies under his white mosquito-bars. He is very weak, but very restless.

"Walt? Are you still there?"

"Right here."

"I closed my eyes for just a moment. When I opened them I was afraid you had gone."

"I won't go, so long as you want me."

"Don't you ever get tired, Walt?"

"A hulk like me? Why should I get tired?"

"But doesn't your hand ever bother you?"

"What do you know about my hand?"

"I heard all about it from the other patients. Some of them were worried about it. They thought the gangrene got into you when your hand was cut, and you've never been so well since."

"It would take more than gangrene to hurt me, lad.

Sometimes these hot days the sun bothers me, and I have to carry an umbrella. But I go to my desk in the Department of the Interior every day, and at night I'm always fine. This is a wonderful night with a full moon. You can see the moonlight across the floor."

"It is very quiet in the ward tonight."

"So many of the men have gone home, you see. And there are no new patients coming in now, thank God. Would you like me to read to you?"

"I can't follow reading. It bothers my head. But I don't like the quiet. Do you think perhaps the nurses will sing in the ward tonight? They do sometimes, now that their work is so much lighter."

"They must have guessed that you wanted them to. One of the nurses is opening the old melodeon now. Another is taking all the lights down to that end of the ward except a single candle."

"I hope she will bring them back later. I don't like to lie alone in the darkness."

"Shall I loop up the mosquito-netting so that you can see the singers?"

"Loop it up for the other fellows too. But then come back here and stay with me. . . . That's fine. I was watching you come and go through the squares of moonlight. It makes your gray head shine like silver."

"Dear son, you will make the old man vain if you go on like that. How this chair creaks when I sit down! Hospital furniture isn't made for the likes of me."

"Walt, I think that young doctor is in love with the nurse who plays the melodeon. Watch him bend over her!"

"A pleasant sight, isn't it? And a pleasant sound as they begin to sing."

"It's good singing for nurses. Are you fond of music, Walt?"

"Fond of a great concert. Fondest of a great singer."

"Have you heard many of them?"

"Many and many of them, at home in New York."

"You told me you lived in Brooklyn."

"So I did. But I went over to Manhattan nearly every day, early or latish. If I planned to go to a concert I started in time to walk for a little while on Broadway. I always liked to stroll up Broadway and view the crowded and mixed humanity. And always some notable."

"Were the notables always worth looking at?"

"For one reason or another I found them so. I remember on a sparkling winter day many years ago I was passing a great house on a corner, a house with a shut-up, secretive look. In front of the door waited a high black sleigh filled with fur robes. The driver in a fur cape reined in two prancing black horses. Just as I came abreast of the house the door flew open. One man ran ahead to the sleigh, and two others helped, almost carried down the steps, a little old man wrapped in furs. It was a great scene of the pride of life, all the prouder somehow because the center of it was so very old, and so frail."

"Was he one of your notables?"

"It was John Jacob Astor the first, Astor of Astoria and the great North fur trade."

"Oh, yes! Washington Irving wrote of him."

"Washington Irving didn't tell of his son John Jacob, shut up in another house and waited on like a baby, John Jacob the second, a helpless, mowing idiot. Yet it, too, fills in the picture."

[169]

"You don't like Washington Irving, Walt, because he wasn't kind to your beloved Dutch in New York. But begin now and tell me about the concerts you heard."

"I heard all the great ones, Mario, Grisi, Jenny Lind. But I remember none of them so well as I remember one night at the opera."

"Go on, tell me all about it."

"I had arranged to take my sister Mat, my brother Jeff's wife. She is a hard-working woman, the mother of children. Dear to her is any kind of treat or expedition. But you see we lived away off in Brooklyn, and late that afternoon there came on a drenching downpour. Mat went about the house from window to window, watching the rain splash into the puddles, watching the sky for a break in the clouds. More than once she said to me, 'Perhaps the rain will let up.' But it didn't let up. She looked at me with a quivering lip, like a child's when it is disappointed."

"But you didn't let her be disappointed, did you?"

"I waited until I could wait no longer. Then I said to her, 'Come on, Mat, it will be dry inside the Opera House.' She rushed into her wraps, and off we paddled. We got on the Brooklyn ferry, looking across at the lights of Manhattan through the rain. Then we got a bus up to the Opera. Because it was a rainy night we were lucky enough to get seats in the front row. We heard the handsome-mouthed Guerrabella. His voice rang in my ears a month afterward."

"Guerrabella! Of course he could sing, with a name like that!"

"When the curtain had fallen we got slowly to our feet, as if we didn't want the opera to end. 'Oh, Walt,'

says Mat, 'I shall think of nothing else for a month!'
'Shan't you?' says I. 'Well, I'm thinking of something
else right now. I'm thinking of supper.' Then she
laughed, and said she was hungry, too. We hadn't had
anything since dinner in Brooklyn at three o'clock.''

"So you went to supper?"

"We had a good oyster supper at Fulton Market,
all the snugger for the rain on the roof. When the
oysters came I ordered two tankards of ale. The waiter
sang out to some one in the background, 'Two ales!'
I cautioned him, 'Ale in tankards.' He looked at me
scornfully, as if I had said something that wasn't real
decent. But he sang out, 'Pewter them ales!' ''

" 'Pewter them ales!' That was funny."

"Mat choked over her oysters. She needed the ale
when she got it. We were very merry during supper.
And to put a cap on everything, when we came out the
rain had stopped. We went home dry and snug, and
the street-lamps made pools of yellow on the gleaming
black of the pavements.''

"Where is she now, your sister Mat?"

"In Brooklyn, at my mother's house, waiting for the
good days to come back."

"Do good days ever come back?"

"They do, my boy. Or if not the same good days,
then better ones.''

"Walt, I like the singing better now than I did at
first. It seems to get faint and far away, and then
grow strong again. But I wouldn't like it if you weren't
here to talk to me."

"Don't let the old man talk too much, Barrett. Or
let him talk if you like, but don't bother to answer
him. Listen to what they are singing now. It isn't sing-

ing like Guerrabella's, but there's a charm in those fresh young voices."

"Let me close my eyes. It makes the words come clearer. I get them all now. I remember this hymn.

" 'My days are gliding swiftly by, and I a pilgrim stranger
Would not detain them as they fly, those hours of toil and
      danger.
For O we stand on Jordan's strand, our friends are passing
      over;
And just before, the shining shore we may almost discover.'

Yes, it seems like that sometimes. It has seemed like that lately."

"Barrett, dear lad, was that a tear? Don't weep, dear son."

"Then talk to me, Walt. Tell me something. Tell me anything."

"Did I ever tell you about finding another lad of your name in another hospital here in Washington?"

"You mean another named Sloane?"

"Not only was the surname the same, but the initial. He was Breckenridge Sloane, and you are Barrett."

"You found Breckenridge Sloane here in a hospital?"

"I see you recognize the name. Perhaps he was a relative?"

"A relative indeed. My only brother."

"I had not guessed that, Barrett. You don't look alike."

"We were never alike in anything. But he was my only brother."

"It is a long time since you last saw him?"

"I haven't seen him since the beginning of the war. Now I shall never see him again."

"I hadn't meant to tell you that, Barrett. Or at least not until you were stronger."

"To tell me what?"

"Lie down, lad, lie down."

"Do you mean Breck is dead?"

"He died last April. Died of his wounds received in battle."

"Poor Breck! But he died for his convictions. That's a good enough fate for any man. Do you happen to know his rank in the army?"

"He was a captain, like you."

"A captain in the Union army, Walt?"

"To be sure. A captain in the Union army."

"Walt, you must have guessed. But I can't let you go on guessing. I can't impose on you any longer. I was—I am—a Confederate soldier."

"Thank God, Barrett, it is 'was' now for all of us."

"But had you guessed?"

"I don't know that I had. I must have, if I thought about the matter. But it makes no difference anyhow."

"It did at first."

"No, it never did. Not the slightest difference."

"Ah, but it's good to hear you say that! Take my hand in yours, Walt. My eyes are tired, but I don't want to lose you when I close them. How sweet the music sounds now, but how faint!"

"Can you go to sleep?"

"It is sleep, or something. You will tell me, won't you, Walt?"

"I will tell you anything I can tell you."

"Is this what they call death?"

"No, dear lad. But if it were, death is nothing to be afraid of."

[173]

"You are sure of that, Walt?"

"Sure of it. When death comes it seems just a matter of course, like eating your breakfast or any other event of the day. I have witnessed hundreds of deaths, and it was always just so quiet and commonplace."

"Were you with my brother when he died?"

"Not just at the last. I was with him the day before. He was wounded at the battle of Five Forks, and brought here to Washington a few days afterward. I saw him every day for two weeks, but he died early in the morning, before I reached the hospital."

"I wish you had been with him. Has the music stopped?

"They have closed the melodeon, and are leaving the ward, all but one nurse. She has put out our one candle. But she cannot put out the full moon. Great squares of moonlight lie on the floor."

"The Government need not waste a candle on a Confederate soldier, Walt. But kiss me good-night before I go to sleep. You may want to leave while I'm —sleeping."

XXIX

1865

TOM SPENCE, JIM THE JANITOR

The same summer evening finds lights
going after hours in a certain office
of the Department of the Interior.
A clerk in his evening aspect of man
about town is rummaging in an un-
locked desk.

"I can't stop your coming in here, maybe. Just the
same, Mr. Spence, you ain't got any right at that desk.
It ain't your desk. It's Mr. Whitman's."

"You aren't paid to debate questions of right and
wrong, Jim."

"I dunno as I like your coming here after hours
anyway. Tain't like you."

"Is that so? Let me tell you I'm subject to call
twenty-four hours a day. A clerk isn't like a janitor,
who gets his job through political pull and can work
at it as little as he chooses."

"That may be so. But I'm going to make it my business to report you to somebody tomorrow."

"A lot of good that will do you. Think I'd be here
at all if it wasn't for orders?"

"Orders? Who from?"

"The big boss. The Secretary of the Interior himself."

"Well, maybe it's all right. I'll stay around here till you get through, and lock up good and tight after you."

"You won't do that either. I've got to get a book out of this desk, and then replace it again before the beginning of office hours tomorrow."

"Why?"

"So that big loafer Whitman won't know it hasn't been in his desk all the time."

"Is that the how of it? Well, it sounds sneaky to me."

"As I've pointed out to you already, Jim, the ethical aspect of the situation is beyond you. But I'm not doing this because I want to. And it's damned unhandy to have to attend to it tonight. It will make me leave Diamond Kitty's an hour early."

"Is that the kind of places you hang around?"

"Like any other bachelor, Jim. Don't you envy me?"

"Not much. You'd better get married."

"Not for me, Jim, to be tied to the same woman all the time, and maybe a pack of squalling brats. Besides—"

"Huh?"

"A man can't marry a quadroon girl, even if he wanted to."

"Oh, then they have quadroon girls at Diamond Kitty's?"

"They have. The prettiest in Washington. And the prettiest of them all is in love with yours truly."

"Well, that's big business, maybe. I don't see it."

"Here's the book safe enough. Must keep it safe

for his Harlanness to get his claws into. 'Leaves of
Grass.' Nice title, eh?"

"It sounds kind of pretty."

"It isn't. I haven't much sympathy with these Methodists from Ioway. But for once the big boss is right."

"How d' you know?"

"I looked into the book myself one night when my
quadroon couldn't take me on. And it's pretty rotten
stuff, Jim. Pretty rotten stuff."

XXX

1865

WILLIAM DOUGLAS O'CONNOR, ELLEN O'CONNOR

It is late afternoon in the furnished parlor which is the best that can be rented in post-war Washington on the salary of chief clerk of the Light House Bureau. Mrs. O'Connor, a Massachusetts woman of frail physique but fine tranquillity, sits sewing on a frock for her little girl. William O'Connor, an Irishman all fire and vocabulary, comes cannoning in.

"You're early today, William."

"Don't see how I can be. Don't know why I should be."

"It's a treat to have you early. Since you've been in the Government service I seldom get you to myself for an hour."

"Government service isn't easy. Blast the fools who think it is!"

"It isn't easy in your hands, William. But nothing ever is easy in your hands. You aren't made that way.

[179]

Won't you sit down? Your favorite chair is waiting for you."

"I feel as if I never wanted to sit down again."

"Haven't things been going well at the office?"

"I haven't been near the office all afternoon."

"What's the trouble? Put down your hat and take a drink of water. Don't try to talk until you're ready. But when you are ready, tell me exactly what the trouble is."

"Nellie, it's Walt."

"Our Walt? Walt Whitman?"

"Nellie, you know Walt as few women ever know a man unless they're married to him. That first year he walked the wards of the army hospitals he practically lived with us."

"I wish we could have kept him after that. But he was afraid of taking too much from any one."

"You lived in the same house with him. Every day you made him sit down at our table for dinner. Did he strike you as a person who isn't fit for decent society?"

"Whatever are you talking about, William? You know I'm as fond of Walt as if he were my own father. And not a common father at that, but the very special sort of father only some few women are lucky enough to have."

"This Walt of ours, Nellie, this infinitely tender soul, who has given his days and nights to succour the wounded and stand by the bed of the dying—"

"I know."

"This warmest, most pitying, most disinterested soul of our time, has been dismissed from a petty Government clerkship."

"Walt dismissed?"

"Wait! That isn't the half! Dismissed as the author of an obscene book. Dismissed by the Secretary of the Interior in person."

"I never liked Secretary Harlan, William. I've heard that President Johnson appointed him because the administration owed so much to the Methodist Church. That strikes me as an unnecessary slur on the Methodists."

"Harlan's the sort of vermin you may find anywhere."

"I don't quite understand this action, though. The book you speak of must be 'Leaves of Grass.' How did Mr. Harlan ever happen to read it? He doesn't strike me as being at all a reading sort of person."

"He read it on purpose to dismiss Walt."

"But how did he get it to read? 'Leaves of Grass' has been out of print for years. The war and Mr. Eldridge's bankruptcy stopped the sale. My guess would be that there aren't three copies in the city of Washington."

"You wouldn't believe how he got it. You wouldn't believe such a thing even of Harlan. Walt had a copy in his desk at the office. He was using it to note changes with an eye to a new edition, if he can ever scrape together the money."

"Surely Mr. Harlan didn't borrow it from Walt?"

"He didn't borrow it. He stole it. He had a clerk take that copy from Walt's desk every night for him to go through. And he had it put back before Walt reached the office every morning, so that Walt shouldn't suspect what was going on."

"What a contemptible trick!"

"This morning he calls Walt in, shows him a list of passages that he has copied from the book, and sacks him on the spot."

"But, William, isn't there any appeal, any redress?"

"The newspaper men are up in arms. They're not so fond of Walt, but this hits their own weak spot. Freedom of the press, and all that. I don't know what form their indignation will take, if any. But I went to see Harlan myself. That's where I've been this afternoon."

"Did you get any satisfaction from him?"

"Only the satisfaction of making him admit what he had done."

"Did he defend his action?"

"He said it was a book he could never think of giving his young daughter to read. That is, if he had a young daughter. There is one child that was lucky never to be born—Harlan's young daughter."

"It's exasperating, William. But, after all, it isn't the end of the world. Walt has been let out of other jobs. He is quite amusing when he gets to telling about his experiences."

"That isn't the point. Walt may possibly get another clerkship, though half the late army is crowding into Washington hungry for anything that pays a salary. But nothing can make up for the rank injustice of what he has suffered. To be turned into the gutter because he is the author of the greatest book ever written in America!"

"You probably take it harder than Walt does himself. I still see a good deal of him off and on. He was in here yesterday before you got home. He came to read me a new poem, which he said was to go into a new volume."

"That's another hope dashed. He undoubtedly meant to publish it himself. Now there will be no new volume."

"It was a very beautiful poem. I have always thought Walt's poems stirring. They enlarge one's grasp of things. But they are not commonly what I should call beautiful."

"He has been after something deeper and more essential. He couldn't stop to concern himself with beauty."

"I don't agree, William. I think he has just dug down to this. I meant to tell you about it last night, but you worked so late I was asleep when you came in. It struck me as very significant. The poem was about President Lincoln."

"That isn't strange. Walt was a forthright Lincoln man. He stood up for Lincoln even in the darkest days, thought him a wonderful specimen of Western manhood, and equal to any crisis."

"More than that, William. Walt loved Lincoln. I believe he never knew him, except as they used to speak in the street. But Walt loves his memory as he loves lilacs, and the evening star, and the song of the hermit thrush."

"How soothing that sounds!"

"That's right, sit down. You are sitting just where Walt sat last night. The dusk drew in earlier than it usually does in June, because it was raining. I had lighted a lamp. Walt sat there with the lamplight shining on his fine gray head, and read me the whole of his poem. It began,

" 'When lilacs last in the dooryard bloomed,
And the great star early drooped in the western sky in the
    night,
I mourned—and yet shall mourn with ever-returning spring.'

You see why I call it beautiful?"

"It was about the death of Lincoln, then?"

"Yes. Walt was in Brooklyn with his mother when the news came. Neither of them ate anything all that day, though they made a pretense of sitting down to meals. Walt bought all the different newspapers as they came out. He would read them in silence and then pass them to his mother. They could not speak even to each other."

"That dreadful day, Nellie! I shall never forget it."

"Nor I. But now I don't want to forget it. I think of it in the spirit of Walt's elegy. I can't remember all of the poem, of course. But I made him read over the last few lines until I learned them.

" 'Comrades mine, and I in the midst, and their memory ever I
    keep—for the dead I loved so well;
For the sweetest, wisest soul of all my days and lands . . . and
    this for his dear sake;
Lilac and star and bird, twined with the chant of my soul,
There in the fragrant pines, and the cedars dusk and dim.'

That was the way it ended."

"Nellie, I tell you I won't have it! I'm not going to let Walt be thrust out by a lot of smug-faced hypocrites. He stands for everything that's finest. He's free and strong and tender. It is time his worth was known and admitted."

"But what can you do about it? Are you going to take his case before the President?"

"Take the case of Walt Whitman before Andrew Johnson? I am not. I'm going to take his case before the American people."

"You think his services to the wounded have endeared him to the people at large?"

"On the contrary, I think they have set him farther than ever from his real object. People tell him he can nurse sick soldiers: he's proved that. But as to writing poetry, they say, he'd better leave that to the real poets, like Mr. Longfellow and Mr. Lowell."

"William, people may feel that way about Walt, though it was you who said they did, not I. But if they feel that way, what good can it do him to take his case before them?"

"It will do this much good, at least. The average American may hate a man who wants to upset his established ideas of things, who asks inconvenient questions and makes him think. But even worse he hates a sneak. The Honorable James Harlan got into the President's cabinet as a Methodist, you tell me. But he will go into history as a sneak."

"Do you think history will have much to say about Mr. Harlan, William?"

"It will remember him only as the man who sacked Walt Whitman. But never mind now about history. The present task is to get this matter plainly before every one whose opinion counts."

"Should you try the newspapers, or would a separate pamphlet be better?"

"Newspapers have to consider questions of policy. A pamphlet alone would have the proper freedom. A pamphlet it must be. But we must get the proper man to do the pamphlet. What should you say to John Burroughs?"

"Walt has no stauncher friend. Burroughs means to write about Walt some day, when he gets around to it. But it takes him forever to get around to anything, and anyhow he isn't a fighter. Burroughs won't do for this job."

"It isn't altogether a question of fight, Nellie. Understanding must precede controversy. Walt is the greatest man of his generation, but his very size makes him clumsy. And it's a queer thing to say about a man who never moves without his notebook, but there are times when I feel that Walt is almost inarticulate."

"Your worst enemy could never say that about you."

"Oh, I know I'm glib!"

"I should say eloquent, William, eloquent and fiery. To be tied to a desk in a Government bureau is a hard destiny for you. But at least when you write of Walt you will be free to say all you think."

"Who says I am going to write of him? I will, of course, if no man can be found who is better suited for the task. But can't you think of some one who will do it more ample justice than I could?"

"William O'Connor, don't try to deceive yourself. You don't deceive me for a moment. Your fingers are simply itching to get at that pamphlet."

"I can see how it might be done and a noble picture conveyed. A giant baffled and misunderstood. A free spirit shamefully shackled by his age. A Gulliver tied in cobwebs. A trumpet-call to ears stopped against it."

"And don't forget, William, our tender friend and quiet housemate."

"I don't see how I'm to bring that in."

"But you mustn't leave it out. That is as much the real Walt as the shriek across the prairie. It's the Walt I myself prefer."

"Confound you, Nellie, you're mixing me all up. A minute ago I saw my pamphlet in letters of fire. Now I don't see anything except Walt reading his poems to you in the lamplight. I'll hazard you were darning his socks while he read it."

"Not his, William, yours. Not socks but a shirt. You may be sure, too, that I stopped while he was reading. But afterward he wanted to know all about my sewing. He even said how lucky you were to have me beside you, to share and soften your lot."

"He would say just that. And I can't leave it out without injustice to him, and I can't put it in without spoiling the pamphlet."

"This is just a suggestion. Couldn't you make it a sort of aside? Perhaps even put it in a footnote?"

"Perhaps. But that doesn't seem just right. My God, girl, I have it! Put it in the title!"

"In the title, William?"

"To be sure. The gentle, gray-haired—I have it to a word! 'The Good Gray Poet!' How's that for a smashing title? Make the pamphlet fiery controversy. Make it the fieriest thing since Junius. And then call it 'The Good Gray Poet.' "

"I like that. It makes me think of Walt as he drops in to talk with us for an hour. He's the one man I know who never stays too long."

"Let me see how it looks on paper. Who's been leaving this stuff on my desk?"

"What stuff? Oh, that's part of my sewing. Give it to me."

" 'The Good Gray Poet.' Rotten pen. . . . Now listen, Nellie. 'The Good Gray Poet. Paragraph. Mr. James Harlan, raised by flattering fortune and Methodist prayers to an eminence he neither deserves nor adorns, has just given signal proof of what nowadays constitutes a statesman.' How is that for a beginning?"

"Not good enough."

"Why not?"

"Too Irish for one thing. Then you're supposed to be writing primarily about Walt, not about Harlan."

"Let it stand for the present. Perhaps I can use it later on."

"You may get quite a bit written after tea, if you find you're not too tired."

"You bring my tea here to my desk. I'm going to spend the evening on Mr. Secretary Harlan."

"Not too violent, William."

"Oh, I shan't call him names! Just boil him in oil, that's all. Boil him in oil, and crown the whole thing with sweetness. 'The Good Gray Poet!' "

XXXI

1870

JOHN BURROUGHS, WALT WHITMAN

*A Sunday morning of late spring, in
the woods near Alexandria. Two men
who have walked out from Washington fling themselves down in a little
clearing.*

"This looks like a good loafing-place, John."

"It looks like more than that. It looks like a treasure-house of Mother Nature."

"You at any rate will find it such. You, John, are a child of the woods, fields, hills. You are native to them in a sense almost of miracle"

"You walk out here often enough yourself, Walt."

"Every Sunday in fine weather, and sometimes during the week, I come in this direction. Yet it is not the woods that draw me so much as it is the river. I have never lived away from a big river."

"You like the steady unhindered flow of water?"

"I like the wharves too, and the shape of boats and smell of shipping. I like sailors and stevedores."

"You like men, in other words. The more I for my part see of men, the better I like to get away from them, as we are away from them here and now."

"Surely that is unjust, John. There's something deep, oh, so deep, in every man, something worth traveling to, waiting for. It is something to be seen, absorbed, respected, yes, reverenced."

"You make out a case for human nature."

"I speak as I have seen."

"Doubtless if a man lives long enough and has enough patience, things will come right in the end. Or even if they don't come right, a man grows too weary to chafe at their going wrong."

"That sounds like before breakfast, John. Or at any rate not like the poet who wrote,

> " 'Serene I fold my arms and wait,
>   Nor care for wind, or tide, or sea:
>   I rave no more 'gainst time or fate,
>   For lo! my own shall come to me.'

And the poetic word is ever the true word."

"Don't you go quoting my poetry at me. If you must quote something quote your own."

"I doubt if I could quote my own poems."

"I know you never do. But is it because you can't, or because you're too proud?"

"My poems are there for any one who wishes to read them. But if you would like a poetic accompaniment to the spring sunshine, I can recite at length from 'The Lady of the Lake.' Or should you prefer 'Marco Bozzaris' because it's shorter? You may have your choice."

"I don't dare make a choice. I've no desire to listen to the old stock poems. You have done your share to spoil them for me."

"It's easy to speak ill of a poem, John. In my time

I've spoken ill of thousands, condemned their mawkishness, thinness, want of flesh and fiber. Yet I would have not fewer poems, but more. I would have poems to embrace the boundless prodigality and amplitude from Maine to California, and the life of a man from his grandfather to his grandson."

"I wish we had brought along a pot of coffee, Walt, or had some way of making it here. . . . But I didn't mean to interrupt you."

"You didn't interrupt. You completed. Good coffee, like good poems, is an alleviation of the human lot. It is also a bond between the people who appreciate it."

"It is, indeed. Just like a taste for the writings of Walt Whitman, or a love of lilacs."

"The lilacs on our way out were very fine, John. I absorbed each one we passed. I have always loved them above all other flowers."

"I know you have.

" 'Lilac blooming perennial, and drooping star in the west.
And thought of him I love.'

You see I can quote you when I like. That's a poem which satisfies even your critics, Walt. It never falters for a second. For once you found words for just what you wanted to say."

"Not quite, John."

"You mean you couldn't say all that was in you even in 'When Lilacs Last in the Dooryard Bloomed'?"

"I mean that for twenty years I've been searching for the word to express what the twilight note of the robin means to me."

"And have never found it?"

"Not yet."

"Then must you go on searching for another twenty years?"

"Twenty, or fifty. It may take fifty, John."

"But don't you ever get discouraged and think, what if there is no such word?"

"That is only another way of saying that the word yet remains to be found, invented."

"I have given up hope of words. I long now only for a retreat where I may possess my soul."

"Do you mean a woodland cabin, such for instance as Henry Thoreau had on the edge of Walden Pond?"

"I mean exactly that."

"Then why not get it? Thoreau did."

"He did. But Thoreau wasn't married."

"What of that? After all, drawbacks constitute at least one element of a man's real strength. I liked Thoreau when he came to see me years ago in Brooklyn. But I feel now that his possession of his own soul was imperfect, or he wouldn't have needed to retire from common society."

"Thoreau was a rebel."

"He was a rebel who confessed weakness. The strong rebel does not flee from conditions. He forces conditions to conform, or else ignores them. He even feeds his spirit on opposition."

"You are a living example of what you preach, Walt. Yet you speak only the half of reality. You must know from observation if not from experience that a man may be fretted to ribbons, and his best work go undone, for want of a little seclusion."

"I grant that if a man have a big piece of work to do, a den to do it in is a great assistance. A statue, for instance, would be easier modeled in a shed to itself than on a corner of the kitchen table. But I won't say it couldn't be done on a corner of the kitchen table. As for poems, I know they may be written there. Some of my own have been."

"I no longer write poems."

"You no longer write verses, you mean, and I for one regret that you do not. Yet what are your jottings or essays but poems, and love poems at that? They are instinct with love for the grass, flowers, trees, for the shell of sky, for the little creatures that go about their own concerns in beautiful disregard of man's sickliness and shames."

"I don't find those things on a corner of the kitchen table, Walt."

"Wherever you find them you may write them down. You see what I have here in my coat pocket."

"Is it a sort of notebook?"

"Three sheets of good paper folded, and sewed firmly together. I have not been without such a packet in twenty years. A book does not begin as a book. It becomes a book only after countless collectings, sortings, shiftings. It begins with a thought at a time. And often the thought must be farther reduced to a single word."

"A book, any book, is an act of faith. Out here in the woods my faith always begins to burn high. It burns highest, I think, when I am out here with you, Walt. Yet I'm surprised to find that you still carry a notebook like a beginner."

"I still am a beginner. I am on the lookout for ever fresh beginnings, each a part of that whole which taken all together they will some day bring into being."

[193]

"I am curious about your fresh beginnings. At least 'Leaves of Grass' must be pretty well finished by this time, even with all your editings and re-editings."

"Even in 'Leaves of Grass' there are changes, corrections, new arrangements and orders. And in 'Drum Taps' also. Taken together they make a fine hefty volume, a body gathering scope as time goes on, gathering maturity and balance."

"It was a fine body as you brought it out in New York three years ago. Is that edition all gone?"

"Gone, but not sold."

"How's that? You never told me anything about it."

"I have had bad luck with my other editions, John. The second was threatened with prosecution, and dropped by the publishers. The third was selling well when the war came on and put a stop to its sale. But this big fourth edition I built hopes on. Thanks to William O'Connor and his valiant championship, they were great hopes."

"You thought people would be anxious to read the work of a man so happily named the Good Gray Poet?"

"I thought half the public would be drawn by William's label. The other half might look eagerly for the passages which made Secretary Harlan cast the good gray poet into outer darkness."

"By the way, what has become of Harlan?"

"He found the outer darkness yawned for him, too."

"Do you think your dismissal had anything to do with his downfall?"

"It may have had. The common American man cares little for poems, I fear, even poems written for the love of him. But his common manhood is revolted when private papers are ransacked stealthily at night, and stealthily replaced."

"So Secretary Harlan has vanished, and Walt Whitman remains?"

"Remains in a better clerkship in another department."

"There's justice in that. But go on about your big edition."

"It was published in New York, and according to my habit I saw it through the press. Then the publisher's office was raided for debt, and my book seized among others. The edition was lost, melted away, sank somehow into the ground. I could never learn what became of it. Perhaps a dozen copies I had by me, and have sold or given away. The rest have vanished."

"But, Walt, you were living in Washington at the time. I was seeing you constantly, often every week, never less than once a month. You never mentioned the loss of your edition. Yet surely you must have resented it."

"I felt it, of course. I do not know that I resented it. William O'Connor resented it for me, was all for having the law on the law, for dragging the books back somehow from the abyss that had swallowed them. Good comes from evil, as you see."

"In what way?"

"A coolness had sprung up between William and me. There had been words about an indifferent subject, Sumner's reconstruction policy, words I spoke in haste and William hotly resented. But when he heard of my trouble he flew to my defense. There never was such a friend in need as William."

"William sees in you his best subject. There are times when I think he values you more as a subject than as a friend."

"He is not an easy man to deal with even now that we are reconciled. I often go to his house when he is not there, to sit and talk quietly with his wife. Yet William has worn himself out in my cause when he might have been advancing his own interests. William not more than you, though, not a bit more."

"Whatever I've done, Walt, has been done freely and gladly."

"I've deserved my enemies, John, but I don't see how I shall ever manage to deserve my friends."

"We are your friends, so say no more about it. Are your legs rested? The sun is getting high. It will be higher before we can reach home, even if we start at once. And the idea of breakfast recommends itself."

"Does Mrs. Burroughs expect us for breakfast?"

"I told her to."

"Will she expect us with buckwheat-cakes, John? And with her incomparable coffee? There never was such coffee as Mrs. Burroughs'."

"How should I know? I don't share your reckless optimism and unbounded faith in the future. You're a man who takes his life as he takes his book, patiently and generously day by day."

"My book and life are one, John. How else could I take them?"

"Well, I'm only a bank examiner who wishes he wasn't. Yet I share your taste for walks in the country, and late leisurely breakfasts, and the song of the hermit thrush."

"And for the joys of comradeship. You should put

[196]

that at the head of the list. John Burroughs the comrade outshines any other, as if in him comradeship were raised to the rank of a special talent."

"It may be the only talent he has. Yet even now something is buzzing in this beehive of a head of his. You are right about Thoreau. His withdrawal was a retreat. But surely a man may get a place of his own in the country, and farm it enough to make a living."

"Surely he may."

"Then in the long winters he may get his books written, and perhaps in time make a living from them if he tires of farming. A shack in the woods on the remote outskirts of a farm, and getting my books written as they come to me: it sounds almost too good to be true, doesn't it?"

"Nothing is too good to be true, John. At the best and truest a thing, however long looked at, just a little eludes us."

"Yes, that's the pity of it."

"Not a pity at all. All the better if it does elude us. Mystery is not the denial of reason, but its fine flower and affirmation."

"And patience is the fine flower of the man. Here you are at fifty, cordial, blithe, gallant, after a life that would have worried any other man to fiddle-strings. I can see it is patience turns the trick."

"Patience and a little notebook, John. It is no good waiting unless a man grows in waiting. And as the man grows the book must grow."

"Then I hope it will be buckwheat-cakes, to strengthen your next edition. Though I believe there are tons of buckwheat-cakes eaten in this country, and only one 'Leaves of Grass' to show for them."

"A good breakfast goes into the result, along with the lilacs and the hermit thrush. Our scheme of things must be large enough to include all a man's needs. It must indeed be all-inclusive, must take in all his weaknesses and disabilities, all, all set down in the sum."

"But, Walt, think a moment. Your scheme of things would include even the sheriff who lost your books for you. It would include even Secretary Harlan."

"It would include even Judas Iscariot. My philosophy sees a place and a time for everybody. And why not, John, why not? All of us are parties to the same bargain."

XXXII

1871

PETER DOYLE, WALT WHITMAN

The steps of a small grocery at Seventh and Pennsylvania Avenues, Washington. It is night. Peter Doyle, who was born in Ireland and served in the Confederate army, is now a street-car conductor. He and his frequent companion have bought a watermelon, and are sitting on the steps of the grocery to eat it.

"That man who just went by was laughing at us, Walt."

"Was he?"

"People generally do, when they see us sit here and eat a melon."

"Never mind, Pete. Let them have their laugh. We have the melon."

"It's a good melon, anyway."

"I am always glad to live through the year, if only to have the melon season come round again."

"This is an awful nice warm night, Walt. Not much like the night when we first met, is it?"

"Did we ever meet? I thought we had always known each other."

[199]

"That was in the middle of the winter, and there was a terrible storm. You were the only passenger on my car. You sat there with a blanket about your shoulders, looking for all the world like an old sea captain."

"I remember now. I had been over to see Burroughs, and was on my way home. You came inside the car and spoke to me, didn't you?"

"I came in and sat down beside you. I was drawn to you somehow. I can't just explain it."

"And I rode with you to the end of the line and back, and then to the end of the line again. And have ridden many times since, haven't I?"

"I wonder sometimes what you see in me to take to, Walt. You could go about with important people if you chose."

"What makes you think that?"

"I've seen 'em talk to you. Only yesterday when you and I were together some one shouted at you from behind, and here when I turned it was General Garfield."

"I knew who it was before I turned. He always shouts the same thing when he sees me, 'After all, not to create only.'"

"What's he mean by that?"

"It's the beginning of one of my poems, Pete. A new poem, published this year."

"Oh!"

"But you have your own share of acquaintances among prominent men, Pete. Aren't you always beckoning President Grant to get on your car?"

"That's as far as it goes. Mornings when I see him

stroll away from the White House on foot I motion him to ride. But he always shakes his head and keeps right on."

"Does he always take those morning strolls in the same direction?"

"He always goes to the same house. On my next trip I see him standing outside the window, leaning on the sill and talking to the old lady."

"She's a widow, isn't she?"

"Yes. She's much liked by men generally. Reckon she's the only person in Washington who can get Grant to loosen up."

"Grant doesn't make friends easily. He is inarticulate, inexpressive. But he, too, feels the need of companionship. It is a need we all feel."

"It's one of the things you talk about in your poems, Walt. But I'm never very sure what you're trying to get at in your poems."

"I am trying to get at just two things."

"What two things?"

"In the first place, all other peoples have their representatives in literature. Only these States, in their boundless prodigality and amplitude, and the American people with their passions, hopes, and struggles, have hitherto contented themselves with something less. Instead of the pure breath and primitiveness of prairies, mountains, the Mississippi, we have put ourselves off with models and lay figures from the British islands."

"You think you can do something about that, Walt?"

"It is a large order, I admit. Yet perhaps on the whole it is less than my second ambition, which

[201]

is to get a complete human being into my books."

"That ought not to be so hard, seems to me."

"Oughtn't it, Pete? You just try it some day and see."

"Oh, I! I'm no scholar. And I don't find it easy to know what I think about things, let alone say it."

"What things, Pete?"

"Big things. The—the Hereafter."

"You are not satisfied with the teaching of your church?"

"It isn't mine so much as it might be. I'm supposed to be a Catholic. But I haven't been in a church in so long I wouldn't know how to act. You don't hold much with churches, Walt?"

"I don't hold with forms, ceremonies. Yet doubtless there is some good in them, or they would not keep men as they do."

"But what about God?"

"There must be something. There can't be a locomotive unless there is somebody to run it."

"And the Hereafter?"

"If a person is the right kind of person, he can't be destroyed in the next world, Pete, or in this."

"But seems to me you think all persons are the right kind of persons."

"Perhaps I do, Pete. Perhaps I do."

"There goes the last of the melon. It was a whale of a good one."

"Should you like to start along home, Pete? You must be tired after your long run."

"It's kind of nice sitting here. This is kind of a nice night."

"It gives a man confidence in greater purposes, doesn't it? The stars look so friendly."

"The sky is full of stars tonight. Begins to look like fall."

"You see the Milky Way, Pete? Star dust to us, but uncounted worlds in themselves, and other worlds beyond."

"Um—m—m."

"There's Orion up there, Orion belted with stars. See the belt and dagger, Pete. And the Great Dipper points to the pole star, the pole star that mariners used to think was given them to steer by. We relate all those things to ourselves, Pete, consider high heaven simply as a sign-board to index our human needs. And right enough, in a way, we are to do it."

"Right enough."

"Earlier in the evening Venus was like a blazing silver well up in the west. Venus and the new moon. But as night advances the great constellation of the Water Serpent stretches its coils over more than half the heavens. The Swan with outspread wings goes flying down the Milky Way. The northern Crown, the Eagle, the Lyre, are all plainly to be made out in their places."

"Venus seems to be growing—tail—like a comet."

"Are you going to sleep, Pete? Your head on my shoulder is like a chunk of lead. It's an awful compliment to my lecturing powers."

"I didn't mean—compliment."

"Sleep for a few minutes, before we get up and march. They are hard days you put in, and old Walt makes a good pillow."

"Good old Walt."

"You love old Walt, even if you don't know what he means? Silence and sleep, dear son? That shows as much as anything. That shows."

XXXIII

1871

ELLEN O'CONNOR, WALT WHITMAN

*Mrs. O'Connor is an ideal audience
both by training and by temperament.
To her little parlor Walt brings his
troubles and his triumphs, as well as
his mending. The session is always
more serene when he finds her alone,
as she is this afternoon.*

"Any socks today, Walt?"

"Do you think I never come here unless I have darning to be done?"

"I hope you always come here when you have."

"I've brought you something a little different today, Nellie. A letter I received in this morning's mail.
There, how's that?"

"A letter from Tennyson! Walt, how splendid!"

"Go on and read it."

"He speaks glowingly of your poems, as if he had
long known and admired them."

"Evidently he has."

"And he wants you to visit him if you ever come
to England. Think of that!"

"It's not bad for Walt Whitman the outcast to be
hobnobbing with the Poet Laureate of England."

[205]

"I don't know what your idea of an outcast may be. Yesterday while I was on a shopping trip I counted three places where your photographs are publicly on sale."

"Yesterday, too, a young lady rose and offered me her seat in a street-car. That is celebrity of another sort. But it is a sort I could get along without."

"Recognition is coming your way at last, Walt. There was Swinburne's poem to you, and Burroughs' book. Then you were asked to deliver the American Institute poem, which you called the 'Song of the Exposition.'"

"Did you like my Institute poem, Nellie?"

"I like all your poems. But I can see that this one is a new sort of triumph.

" 'Blazoned with Shakespeare's purple page,
    And dirged by Tennyson's sweet sad rhyme.'

It proves that you can play the conventional lyre when you care to."

"It is being brought out as a pamphlet by Roberts Brothers in Boston. I myself am bringing out twenty-three new poems and some old ones in another pamphlet, 'Passage to India.'"

"This is a year of great activity in your publications. There's a new 'Leaves of Grass,' too, isn't there?"

"A small edition."

"And the prose book, 'Democratic Vistas'?"

"Yes. But that's prose. And you know, Nellie, no one gives a damn about my prose."

"Give them time to grow into it. Time was needed for the appreciation of 'Leaves of Grass.'"

"How patient a man might be, if he could always feel that time is on his side!"

"You should feel that it is on yours. Look at all this English appreciation!"

"And French, Nellie, and German."

"Good!"

"And now I am being translated even into Danish. By a fellow named Schmidt. I wonder what there is Danish about him."

"The tide has turned, you see. You have only to wait for it to grow fuller and fuller."

"I suppose I'm ungrateful. Yet this very appreciation, coming after all my years of hunger, has set me wondering. Is it worth a man's while to grow old in loneliness, just to have his words put into a language that he himself can't read?"

"Loneliness is the common human lot, Walt."

"I dare say it is. But shouldn't I be less lonely if I had married like another man?"

"Should you?"

"Marriage is a stand-by in a shifting world."

"It is a stand-by, to be sure. Just the same we must pay the price for it, as we pay for everything else. And in your case, Walt, the price might have been too high."

"It would have been high, no doubt. If I had been caught young there would have been no fifth edition of a book that didn't sell the first four, and no letter of invitation from Tennyson. Yet there might have been compensations."

"Walt, have you been seeing her again lately? I mean the pretty woman you used to write poems to a few years ago. The woman for whom you wrote,

" 'I heard you, solemn-sweet pipes of the organ?'

The woman with the brute of a husband."

"That poem has just been translated into Provençal, Nellie."

"It was more of a love poem than anything else you ever wrote. Have you seen the woman lately?"

"I never see her any more."

"Never, Walt?"

"It was painful for both of us to go on meeting. I felt that I depended too much on seeing her, lived only with our meetings in view. Yet she was a beautiful woman, soft-voiced, brown-eyed, very sweet and feminine in all her ways."

"Of course she knew that you admired her?"

"I made no secret of our friendship. Friendship was what it chiefly amounted to. But once it flamed out into a feeling of defense. Her husband opened a letter I had written her, such a letter as I might have written you or Burroughs. But he made an ugly scene about it in front of me and a fourth person, a woman friend of hers."

"How painful for you!"

"How more than painful for her! I tell you, Nellie, if she were free I would marry that woman tomorrow."

"You would marry her out of pity? Or have you really a stronger feeling for her?"

"Love, Nellie,— But I don't want to shock you."

"You never shock me."

"I don't, eh? Then I must often disappoint you. This time I was only going to say, love and marriage are two different things."

"They are, indeed."

"No one can escape love. That is out of the question. But I have escaped marriage. Only sometimes I feel that it has escaped me instead."

"I somehow can't imagine you a married man. Isn't it your habit to spend all your evenings at your office?"

"Well, you see the office is always warm. I have a good gas-lamp, which I bought myself. I use that in the office, and the Government pays for the gas. Then our office library contains many books that I have long wanted to read. And if I want new books, the library will get me anything within reason."

"You have gone back to your old habits of reading?"

"I read now with greater relish than ever, though at a slower rate. I have become middle-aged, Nellie, and I fear prudent. For the first time in my life I am saving money. I send my mother a little every week, and sometimes send a little to my sister Han in Vermont. Han has a bad husband; he long ago settled back on what her family could do for them."

"Still, you manage to save money."

"I am getting a good salary for a single man. I draw sixteen hundred dollars a year."

"After all, Walt, you are very comfortably off now. And you would scarcely like to be left with nothing to desire."

"There is one thing I desire more than all others. But I don't see my way clear to it."

"What is that?"

"A truer reconciliation with William."

"But I thought you and William had made up your

difference. You quarrelled over a politician, but you were reconciled over a publisher."

"That is the affair in outline. But I can account neither for the warmth of our quarrel nor the coolness of our reconciliation. I have sometimes thought there is some cause of misunderstanding which I have not recognized."

"I'm afraid you're right, Walt. Of course William is easily exasperated. The failure of his novel, 'Harrington,' still rankles after all these years, forbids him to try his hand at another. Then his everyday work wears on him. But making every allowance for William's temper, perhaps he has grounds for feeling hard toward you. He thinks you have not appreciated his championship of you."

"I not appreciate William?"

"I am not making the charge against you. That is what he thinks."

"But, Nellie, you don't feel that he is right?"

"I am quite neutral. You've never asked anybody to champion you. When they do, you accept their championship as your right. And, after all, why not?"

"All my champions are dear to me, but William dearer than the rest, because the first and fieriest. But my most understanding champion was a woman."

"A woman, Walt?"

"She wrote of me anonymously last year in the Boston *Radical*. 'A Woman's Estimate of Walt Whitman,' her article was called."

"I remember seeing it. Did you ever find out who she was?"

"She is English. A Mrs. Gilchrist, a widow, author of a Life of William Blake. She had read William Rossetti's selection from my poems. Rossetti described her to me in his letters. A splendid, courageous woman, a mother, qualified by her life as well as by her taste and education to appreciate my poems."

"Did you write and thank her for her appreciation?"

"Of course I did. I have heard from her several times since. She writes most beautiful letters."

"Did you send her your picture?"

"What if I did? What are you laughing at, Nellie?"

"A widow, and a fervent admirer! You're not so safe as you fancy, for all your gray beard and cautious habits."

"That's nonsense. Anyhow, she is in England. And I've no present intention of going to England, even to see Tennyson."

"Right as ever, Walt. Keep something between you and every woman who admires you. Either an indignant husband or the Atlantic Ocean."

"If I had been caught young, I should have married like anybody else. And I should be used to it by this time."

"But you're not young, and you don't want to be. I see your point, Walt. I even sympathize. If I ask you to stay to tea, will you try to be indulgent to William? He was caught young, and caught fatally. And no one has ever written to him from England in praise of 'Harrington.' He sees in you what he himself has missed. Will you remember that?"

"William has right at his elbow something choicer than English praise of a dozen 'Harringtons.' And I sometimes wonder whether he quite appreciates what he has."

"Hush, Walt! I think I hear William's step now."

"I don't hear it."

"Then hush anyhow. I shan't listen to you saying a thing that I don't allow myself to say even to myself."

XXXIV

1872

LOUISA VAN VELSOR WHITMAN, WALT WHITMAN, EDDIE

In the familiar kitchen of the widow Whitman's house in Brooklyn Walt spends the morning hours of a leave of absence from Washington. He comes down to breakfast when he pleases, but Mrs. Whitman delays her own meal until he appears. Eddie, the youngest of Mrs. Whitman's many children, grinds the coffee. Speech and mental life have been denied Eddie from the beginning. But he eyes his mother and Walt as a fond dog might, and grinds coffee until they have to stop him.

"Good-morning, Mother. A nipping morning, isn't it?"

"It's not bad for this time of year. We must expect cold weather in February. But you are used to it warmer in Washington."

"Even in Washington we hug the fire pretty close these days."

[213]

"Have you a fire in your room in Washington, Walt?"

"I have when I want it. I am not often in my room. Evenings I usually go back to my office and write and read. That is in winter. In warm weather I often lounge about the streets or walk in the country."

"You buy all your meals at a restaurant, Walt? You're getting to be a real old bachelor."

"That's your fault. You've spoiled me for other women, Mother, just as your cooking has spoiled me for other cooking."

"I'm glad you still like my cooking. But you shouldn't try to flatter my vanity. An old woman like me!"

"An old woman the young women would do well to pattern after. Besides, other things being equal, the old woman is always more beautiful than the young woman."

"Thee has a way of saying queer things. Sometimes I think thee almost believes them."

"They are true things. That is what makes them sound queer. Do I see buckwheat-cakes and eggs?"

"Everything is ready. Sit right down at the table."

"But your breakfast, Mother?"

"I will sit down with you. I waited on purpose."

"You shouldn't have waited. I suppose you've been up since dawn."

"Since before dawn, Walt. Dawn is late these days."

"Mother, isn't it time Eddie stopped grinding coffee? The coffee is ready in the pot."

"Sometimes he grinds on all morning. He likes to do it."

"Ah, poor Eddie! It's not much comfort you've had from your children."

"It's all the comfort I've had in the world. Sometimes I can find it in my heart to be thankful that poor Eddie never grew up and left me. See, he knows that we are talking about him. He always knows his own name on his good days. Put the coffee-mill down, Eddie. Come and eat your breakfast."

"I think after breakfast I'll stop down here and write a while. It's cold upstairs."

"Eh, Walt. You have still more writing to do?"

"I must get the last of the new poems ready for the new book. It has to be completely finished before I can go back to Washington. Look here, what do you think of this for a color?"

" 'Tis a pretty red, Walt. Or is it green?"

"Ah, you color-blind Quakers! It's a good strong rich green. My new book will be bound in this dark green cloth. Last year's was in light green paper. I like this better."

"I've no wish to be harsh with thee, Walt. But it seems to me that a grown man might do better with his time than go fooling with bits of colored cloth."

"You say that because you know how becoming your white cap is to you. If it wasn't you'd find a good reason for changing, a reason that would suit even your Quaker conscience."

"I've always worn such a cap."

"Perhaps you think I've never noticed it? Perhaps you don't know that when I really want to compliment an old lady in a white cap, I say she looks Velsorish?"

"You're making a good breakfast, Walt, for all your talking. Shall you be here for dinner?"

"Perhaps not. I must go to the printer's to work on

[215]

my proof. I can always do the proof better if I can talk directly to the printer who does my work. Anyhow I like the atmosphere of the shop. I never feel more at home anywhere than in a printer's shop."

"But thee doesn't always come straight home from the printer's."

"I seize the chance of a run about New York. Often I have a bus ride. There are still some of the old drivers left on the Broadway buses. I miss them in Washington. I have many friends there among the street-car men. One of them, Peter Doyle, is almost like a son to me. But take them all in all, they aren't up to the bus drivers. They lack the full fine flavor."

"Whatever do you find to talk to them about?"

"Much the same things I talk about to you. Much the same things I talk about to everybody. Last week for instance I saw 'Julius Cæsar' at Wallack's. Davenport was in it, and a lot of swells. George Storms, the bus driver, can and does talk about 'Julius Cæsar' quite as well, barring grammar, as my friend Van Slyke, with whom I dined last night at his house on Fifth Avenue."

"So that was where thee had dinner yesterday? I had gone to bed when thee came in."

"I should hope you had, Louisa. He gave me dinner at eight o'clock."

"At eight in the evening, Walt?"

"Exactly. It was a lengthy dinner, too. I don't quite know what keeps Van Slyke's dinner from lapping over into the next day. But you should have seen your printer son last night. A nigger waiter stood behind his chair, and another behind his host's. Everything was in the loudest sort of style, dishes with silver covers and wines in silver coolers."

"A great display of worldliness, wasn't it?"

"Worldly enough in its way. But Van Slyke himself is just one of the manliest, jovialest, best sort of fellows. No airs about him."

"I dare say the silver dishes and colored waiters are his wife's idea."

"He has no wife. He lives all alone in that great house, except for the servants who wait upon him. He has a fine library, too, and everything to his taste. He asked me last night to make my home with him."

"That would be a good home for you, Walt. I dare say he has a fire in every room."

"Well, I'm not going there."

"Not at all?"

"Not to live. I dare say when it's handy I shall go there quite often to drink his wine and read his books. But I never could be happy inside a fence. You know that."

"I'm just as well pleased to hear you say it."

"Don't feel obliged to move everything off the table. Half a table is enough for my papers."

"Thee still has such terrible scraps of papers. If thee will insist on writing, why doesn't thee get some good foolscap?"

"As I've explained to you more than once, woman, these scraps of paper are only my first notes. I tie them in bundles and lay them aside for a time. Then when I read them over, if they sound all right, I make a good copy on paper as nice as any one uses."

"You write everything twice? That seems like going to a great deal of trouble."

"A great deal of trouble to very little purpose, eh? You look out, Mrs. Whitman. If you aren't more careful to keep on the right side of me, I shall put you down in my writings. And there you'll stand, white cap and pink cheeks and all, for future generations to read about."

"Thee bothers too much about the future. After all, it's no concern of ours."

"Now you're joining the ranks of the enemy. Did you see the squib about me in yesterday's New York *World?* I have the clipping somewhere. Here it is, in my pocket. 'Walt Whitman was in town yesterday, carrying the blue cotton umbrella of the future.'"

"What is funny in that? Day before yesterday was very stormy, I remember. Rain and sleet, and then snow. Any man in his senses would carry an umbrella—"

"So I thought."

"That is, if he had an umbrella to carry. Probably the man who wrote that silly piece in the paper doesn't own an umbrella."

"The umbrella of the prophet doesn't strike you at all, Louisa? Doesn't draw even one little smile?"

"I can't see what you find in it to laugh at. You make an awful noise when you laugh. See Eddie look at you."

"You will miss my noise when I go back to Washington."

"Aye, Walt. I've always hoped we should have a little place somewhere together. We used often to speak of it. But it looks more as if I might go over to George's in New Jersey. I'm not the woman I was. I'm getting old."

"Don't you give up yet awhile. I may not speak so often of a home for you and me, but I haven't given up the idea. You know I like Washington. Life there is seen more richly and variously than anywhere else on the American continent. But Brooklyn is always 'home' to me. I keep on in Washington because this clerkship is not too hard, and gives me plenty of time for my own concerns. And on the salary I can save money."

"Thee is always generous with what thee has. But if thee is saving money, that is new business for Walt Whitman."

"Just to save money is no pleasure. But to save for a little shack in the country, where Eddie might keep chickens, and you could get my breakfast every morning, and the girls could come and visit us, Mary and poor Han, away from that bad husband of hers—"

" 'Tis a pleasant picture, Walt."

"A year or two more will see it a reality. You watch."

"Even a year or two more is not to be depended on at my age."

"There you are beginning again about your age, just so that I will compliment you. The vanity of you old women! And you a Quaker into the bargain!"

XXXV

1872

TWO DARTMOUTH SENIORS

Early on the morning of Commencement, two youths about to be graduated are seizing their last opportunity to talk things over.

"Well, it's good-by to everything in a few minutes now, Tom."

"I suppose we'll live through it. Don't try to be sentimental."

"Don't you try to be stubborn. You know you're sorry to leave."

"Not so sorry to leave. Shall be sorry to go to work, perhaps. The pit is yawning for me. Papa insinuated as much last night."

"It's yawning for all of us. We're stepping into the Problem of Life. It's been a glorious year, though."

"What made it glorious?"

"We did. The senior class. The old system of class societies was obsolete. Half the time a student didn't know what society he belonged to until it was time to vote at senior elections. But Captain Cotton's Cadets has run things properly."

"By that I suppose you mean improperly."

"Well, we weren't precisely the evangelical set.

[221]

We've had the evangelicals by the ears for months.
Our getting Walt Whitman here to deliver the Commencement poem was the crowning stroke."

"He seemed to be a nice old feller. I sat near him
at the concert in the evening, and he was enjoying himself like a child at a picnic. He's a handsome boy, too."

"What did you think of his poem?"

"I was near the back of the church, and his voice
didn't carry to where I sat. I heard the first line.

"'As a strong bird on pinions free.'

Then his voice seemed to waver, and I didn't get
much more."

"It was his usual stuff, about what a great country
this is, and how much greater it's going to be."

"You call that his usual stuff? I guess you never saw
one of his books."

"Sure, I have. But I don't read with my eye peeled
for naughty words, like some disgusting little boys I
know."

"All the old ladies were in a flutter to see him. They
thought he'd charge in like a bull and spill a lot of bad
language. But the most exciting thing he did was not to
wear any necktie. Nobody heard much of the poem, and
nobody was sure he had finished until they saw the
chairman reach over and shake hands with him."

"Still, we got him here. The fact that he was here
at all must have been wormwood to the faculty."

"Don't flatter yourself it was wormwood. They sent
him to stay at Dr. Leeds'."

"Not Dr. Leeds, the college pastor's?"

"Sure. There isn't any other that I know of."

"But I thought Dr. Leeds was in Europe."

"He is. Whitman stayed with Mrs. Leeds."

"Surely that was a naughty little triumph."

"It was not. My mother called on Mrs. Leeds yesterday. They're old school friends, and Mamma always goes there when she's in town. Mrs. Leeds told Mamma that Whitman was the nicest guest she had ever had in her house. He was quiet and courteous, and everything suited him."

"You mean he didn't show off at all? Didn't do anything peculiar or conceited?"

"He gave her a copy of his poem when he left, if you call that anything."

"I'm free to own that I'm disappointed. Here we organized the senior class, and dared the faculty all the year. The sole result of our efforts is that we gave an audience for a few minutes to the American Homer."

"The American Homer? Who says he is?"

"He says so himself. Or so I've heard."

"I don't believe everything I hear about him. I thought he'd be a compound of Rabelais and a long-shoreman and Murger's 'Vie de Bohême' and the spicy spots in the Old Testament. Instead, he's like some one's old uncle from the country."

"I never had any uncles who were so good-natured or so good-looking. He's a nice old feller."

"I guess it's time we were getting a move on. We mustn't be tardy in beginning the Problem of Life. After today the future is in our hands. Walt Whitman says so."

"That shows how much you understand poetry, for all your college education. The future is in the hands of the future. That's what he says."

XXXVI

1872

JOHN BOYLE O'REILLY, WALT WHITMAN

A Sunday afternoon in Mr. Shaw's house in Boston. The show-rooms, which contain a fine collection of curios, are open to a favored few. A broad-backed man standing in absorption before a fine display of Oriental arms is touched on the shoulder by the erstwhile poet and rebel, John Boyle O'Reilly, now walking abroad in respectability as editor of the Boston Pilot.

"I thought I couldn't be mistaken in that good gray head. But I'd no idea you were in Boston."

"It's great good luck meeting you here, Boyle."

"You trust too much to luck."

"Not at all. I called at your house early in the afternoon. But you had gone out, and your family gave me no assurance that you'd ever be back."

"I've been in one of my restless moods. I wanted to get out and get away."

"To get away from yourself, Boyle?"

"From myself, I suppose."

"It can't be done."

"It has been done. I did it. Only in this case the cure was worse than the disease. I got away from Boyle O'Reilly, but I got into the heart of a Boston Sunday."

"But this house is a very interesting place to spend an hour, Sunday or week day."

"This house isn't Boston. It's an escape from Boston. I am free to come and go here without being announced, and I often take refuge with Mr. Shaw's collection. It reminds me of my own wandering days."

"You put your wanderings in the past? That sounds very settled."

"I am settled, old footloose. Don't rub it in. I see you still come and go as you please. Or at least you come from Washington up to Boston."

"Boston is on my way home, as it happens. I've been up in New Hampshire and Vermont. I took Vermont in passing, to see my poor sister Han, who is married to a man up there."

"Then your objective was New Hampshire? What the devil were you doing in New Hampshire?"

"I went there by invitation. The senior class of Dartmouth College asked me to write and deliver their Commencement poem. Didn't the *Pilot* have the news?"

"I'm afraid not. We've been too busy with Presidential year."

"Let me give you a copy of the poem."

"Oh, thank you! It's already printed, then?"

"My private print. But I expect it to be noticed, and possibly run, in the Washington papers."

"Yes, I suppose they would consider it news. They

must look on you by this time as a regular Washingtonian. This looks good.

> "'As a strong bird on pinions free,
>   Joyous, the amplest spaces heavenward cleaving,
>   Such be the thought I'd think to-day of thee, America.'

I will put it away to read later. Let's sit down now and talk for a few minutes. How did the college strike you, and the town—I forget its name?"

"Hanover. A quiet New England village, very peaceful and self-contained. It interested me to be there for three days, and in all that time never see an African."

"Oh, yes! You're accustomed to blacks in Washington."

"I loved the college lads, Boyle. These vivid young fellows we grow so many of nowadays, earnest, astute, clarified, seeking progress, progress, progress—I sometime wonder where they are going to lead us to."

"They will lead us nowhere. Their fire will be quenched soon enough. But they are fiery as yet, or they would never have invited you to write and deliver a poem for them."

"I suspect they asked me as an insult to college authority. But I seized the chance to affirm once more my poetical principles."

"The new free poetry of America, and the coming American bard? Are you still on that track, Walt?"

"Still, and shall continue on it. Support gathers slowly, Boyle. But it gathers. Word comes to me now and again, from England, from the Continent, and of course from Ireland."

"From everywhere but America, in fact? That is the fate of the American bard and prophet."

"I hope not, Boyle. Yet I found the seniors of Dartmouth but mildly interested in my ideas."

"They liked you personally, didn't they? They took to you, as young men always do?"

"As an audience I had found them cold. But when I got together with a few of them, our feet under a table and the hour growing late and mellow, I felt the electric current begin to flow."

"They came to scoff, and remained to talk all night?"

"For whatever reason they came, they brought me something, and I think took away something in exchange."

"Perhaps they will always remember those hours."

"I hope they may. As for their holding me a taunt against authority, that was but an error of eager youth. I am not a taunt against authority, but a fact coexisting with it. As facts we must both be accepted. In a sense I, too, accept authority."

"Nonsense, Walt. You never accept authority. You simple exist outside it."

"I feel no conflict between outside authority and a free nature. But perhaps that is the wisdom of years."

"Perhaps it is simply your good fortune."

"You, on the other hand, have been brought sharply into conflict with authority. But then you are a rebel by instinct, Boyle."

"Bear in mind, Walt, I grew up under an authority so crushing that a man must either rebel or go under. At the age when your friends in New Hampshire can express their contempt for tradition by asking Walt

Whitman to write a poem for them, I had already been arrested, jailed, tried by the pretense of justice, and shipped as a convict to Australia."

"You were brought early to the boiling-point."

"Early. As a lad of nineteen I was shut up for four months in the hulk of a prison ship, seeing no face but a drunken jailer's, never viewing the light of day except when once a week I was brought on deck to listen to the prayers of an alien church. I suppose I shall never quite cool down."

"The system was cruel, unbelievably cruel. But didn't you find that the men set over you rose superior to the system? There is an inherent goodness in all men, just as there is an inherent vice and folly in all systems."

"There was no goodness of any kind in those men. Nothing but rottenness all the way through. Nothing but brutality, cowardice, treachery."

"Strong words, Boyle. Strong words."

"I remember once when I was working on a road gang in Australia. We slaved all day under the pitiless sun, forbidden to speak to one another while we worked. An overseer with a loaded gun was seated where he could watch our slightest movements. The bread furnished us was spoiled, moldy, some of it crawling with worms. Hungry as we were, we could not eat it. Ground down as we were, we decided to complain. I was elected to present our complaint."

"And perhaps to represent the men, Boyle. I can imagine you at twenty, simple, noble, confiding. Your comrades saw their better selves in you, knew that to your qualities even tyranny itself must listen."

"The overseer did not listen. He did not answer,

would not even look at me. I stumbled through a few
sentences of my complaint, schooling myself to be
humble. All at once he raised his hand and struck me
in the mouth."

"He struck you undefended?"

"Struck me and knocked me down. Left me stran-
gling in blood and dust. I raised myself on my elbow
in time to see him lift the stock of his gun like a club.
Then he brought that down with all his strength on my
head."

"Can such things happen? Under the smiling sky of
heaven, can they happen?"

"They not only happen. They are calculated. They
are a part of the system."

"But you, Boyle, the best sort of young man, the
plain elect—why should even tyranny come at you to
annul, to destroy, to crush?"

"If there is a reason, because even tyranny must
learn that there is one thing it cannot crush."

"You mean man's unconquerable faith?"

"I mean man's undying resentment."

"But the final result even of tyranny has been to
light in you a fire that cannot be quenched."

"The fire was always there, Walt. But it smolders
now instead of burning with a clear flame."

"To burn with a clear flame is a destiny that is given
to few of us."

"You say that as if you mean more than that. Perhaps few of us allow ourselves to burn with a clear
flame."

"That is my idea, indeed."

"It's true enough. Yet in spite of man's best efforts
to wreck himself, in spite of destiny and the devil, we

find now and then a clear flamelike spirit. Have you seen Mr. Shaw's Millet?"

"I don't recognize it by name. What is it?"

"Millet is a painter. A Frenchman, but curiously un-French. When I saw this picture it somehow made me think of you. The subject is very simple. It shows a peasant girl holding a cow by the halter while it bends its head to drink."

"I have my share of sympathy with common men and common things—and perhaps with common cows. But I do not adore the rustic as Burns does, or Whittier."

"The rustic is the people, Walt."

"He is not the people. He is but the beginning of the people, and a miserable beginning at that. He is not equi-large with civilization."

"Yes, he is. He is just that, when Millet paints him."

"You rouse my curiosity. Some day I must look into the matter."

"Your 'some day' is misplaced patience, Walt."

"It is my usual procrastination. Yet it is not only that either. Today is too full of Boyle O'Reilly to contain anything else."

"I love you for saying so. But you need an antidote to Boyle O'Reilly."

"Let me be judge of that."

"You shall be. The Millet picture hangs in the next room to us. I'll just open the door and give you a flash of it. Then you shall judge. There you have it."

"Yes, I—have it."

"It draws you close, I see. A peasant girl, a rustic. Yet it draws you, whether you like it or not."

"Here you, Boyle, I want you to go away."

"Do you mean that?"

"I mean it."

"I've no objection to going, Walt, if I can see you again later on. Will you come up to my house for supper? Or come down tomorrow to the office of the *Pilot?*"

"Yes."

"Yes to which?"

"Either or both. Yes, thankfully, to both. But now get out. I want you to leave me alone for an hour. I want to be alone here with that picture."

XXXVII

1873

ELLEN O'CONNOR, PETER DOYLE

On a gray winter morning Mrs. O'Connor opens her door to Walt's conductor friend, Peter Doyle.

"Oh, good-morning, Peter! I didn't know you for a minute. You don't look quite natural without Walt. Won't you come in?"

"Isn't Mr. O'Connor here?"

"Mr. O'Connor left for the office an hour ago."

"As long as that? I must be mixed on the time."

"You can find him at his office, if it's anything urgent. But won't you sit down and rest for a few minutes? You look tired."

"Thank you, ma'am. I will sit down. I'm upset-like."

"Have you come with a message from Walt? If you have, you may leave it with me and spare yourself a farther trip."

"I suppose I could tell you, ma'am. But I don't exactly like to."

"If it's a message from Walt, I can make allowances. I always do make allowances for him."

"I've no message, and maybe I shouldn't have come. But I've always heard him speak of Mrs. O'Connor friendly-like. And once you're Walt's friend you're his friend always."

"Of course I'm his friend. He was in here to see me only two or three days ago."

"How did you think he seemed?"

"He didn't look well, but he was very cheerful. He told me all about his good boarding-place, and the reading he gets through of an evening."

"That was his account."

"Yes. Walt shows his age lately. He has never been the same man physically since his service in the army hospitals."

"He never will be the same man again."

"Peter, he isn't dead?"

"No, ma'am. Not dead."

"How you startled me! I thought for a minute that was what you meant."

"He isn't dead, Mrs. O'Connor. But he might better be."

"You mean he is ill, hurt, in trouble of some kind?"

"He has had a stroke."

"What sort of stroke?"

"He's paralyzed. He can't move his left arm or leg."

"How dreadful! When did this happen?"

"Last night, in the night. He hadn't felt so well when he went to bed. In the night he woke and couldn't stir. But he tried to make himself believe it was nothing, and went back to sleep."

"He would do just that."

"I stopped in this morning to see him, same as I often do. It was me that found him, helpless."

"Helpless, and all alone? Oh, how pitiful!"

"I've never thought to pity Walt, Mrs. O'Connor.

Most of us are what we have to be. But he was what he wanted to be."

"Did you read Walt's poem which he published last year, 'As a strong bird on pinions free'?"

"I never made much out of his poems."

"But that was what he was himself, Peter. A strong bird on pinions free."

"Yes'm. That's what he was. And now to see him brought low like this!"

"I will go back with you to his room, Peter. Will you wait while I get together a few things that may be useful?"

"I know he'd be glad to see you, Mrs. O'Connor. But what could you do if you did go down there?"

"What his mother might do if she were here. Poor old lady, she has gone over to Camden in New Jersey to live with another son. Lately Walt has feared that she was failing fast. Perhaps she won't even be able to come to Washington and nurse him."

"I'll nurse him, Mrs. O'Connor. It isn't the work of nursing him that I'm afraid of. It's the hopelessness of the whole thing."

"We mustn't give way to despair, Peter. Walt is a strong man. He may rally from this, and live for years."

"I don't think his worst enemy would wish him that, ma'am. A stroke is the beginning of the end. When a strong man has been taken that way, the end can't be too soon in coming."

XXXVIII

1874

GEORGE WHITMAN, MRS. GEORGE WHITMAN ("LOU")

Since he came North at the time of his mother's death, Walt has continued to live in Camden, New Jersey. He is a member of his brother George's household, under the direct charge of his sister-in-law Lou. George Whitman is now finishing his first home-cooked meal since his return from a business trip.

"That was a good steak, Lou. They don't know how to cook a steak in hotels."

"You miss my cooking when you're away from home?"

"Yes."

"Don't you miss anything else?"

"Of course I do. I miss a lot of things. But you can't expect me to keep talking about them like a damned bridegroom."

"I needn't expect it, I know. Have you quite finished your dinner?"

"Um-hum."

[237]

"Then aren't you going up to see Walt? He has asked more than once when you would get back from your trip."

"I know I ought to go."

"Why do you speak in that tone, George? Walt is always good company. When I go in to see him he chats to me in the pleasantest way."

"I dare say you get a good deal of him."

"Not too much. If I don't seek him he never bothers me. No one could be less trouble in a house than he is. That's really remarkable, when you consider how sick he has been, and how his lameness clings."

"He may chat to you. He never chats to me."

"Then mayn't that be partly your fault? Perhaps it's hardly natural for brothers to talk politely like strangers. But I remember your mother used to say you were like your father, and he never had much to say to anybody."

"God knows Walt don't suffer in that way. He'll buzz any vagabond in the street, and ask 'em into the house too. Talk to 'em and give 'em good advice. I'm sure I don't know what you do when I'm not here."

"Do about what, George?"

"About his picking up people."

"He calls people in here when he can't get out, as he often can't. He had a couple of men up in his room this morning before you got here. Ferrymen I think they were. Rough-looking customers, but civil enough to me."

"He ought not to ask such people in the house. He must know you don't like it."

"I don't like it, George. I mind what the neighbors will think. But I can't blame Walt so much either.

Here he is unable some days even to stir from an upstairs room, and his own brother comes home from a journey and sits down to dinner without even going in to say 'Howdy' to him."

"Look here, Lou, it isn't that I'm not fond of Walt. But I just can't bear to see him as he is now. He was the hero of my boyhood, and as I grew older I went on looking up to him as the flower of the family. I'll own I'm disappointed in what he's made of his life. Writing poems that nobody wants to read strikes me as no fulfilment at all of his early promise."

"Some people must have read his poems."

"Damned few. Don't see myself why anybody should want to read 'em. Just the same, it's too much for me to see him now, and realize that he's done for."

"Surely you take too gloomy a view of his case. Why should you despair on his account, when he doesn't despair himself? He is cheerful enough."

"He's only trying to hide his feelings from you. He wouldn't let a woman, any woman, see how downhearted he is."

"That may have been true at one time, George. At first he was hurt and bewildered. He had always made so much of health, you see. He had felt his own strength, and tried to share it with the less fortunate. He couldn't get used to the idea of being a sick man."

"Of course Mother's death affected him powerfully. Mother was devoted to all her family, but Walt was closer to her than the rest of us."

"It was very touching, George, when he was first taken ill in Washington and feared he might not live, how he made that little will. Only three or four scribbled lines, leaving his gold watch to his mother, because he had nothing else to leave."

"He'd the savings he pays us his board out of. Wonder why he never thought to mention them?"

"Then Jeff's wife died just before your mother. Walt was fonder of Jeff's wife than he is of George's. But he always tries to be considerate of me. For a sick man he succeeds very well."

"I'm glad he tries to make the best of the situation."

"Not only that, George. He looks for the situation itself to improve."

"Expects to grow a new leg in place of the lame one, does he?"

"No. But he thinks he will mind his lameness less when he gets a little place of his own, and is no longer dependent on other people's forbearance."

"A little place of his own? It would be a very little place, I think."

"He has always paid his way with us. He must have something."

"Whatever he has, it's been getting less right along. Even a small house would cost more money than he can possibly have."

"He expects to make some money from a new edition of his poems."

"A new edition? My God! The old ones didn't sell. Even the few readers he once had must have forgotten the poor old man by this time. He thinks he's going to make money out of 'Leaves of Grass'? That's nothing but a delusion."

"He is counting on it quite confidently. In another year or two he hopes to get out his new edition."

"He tells you all this stuff? And you have to sit and listen?"

"I like to have him talk of his writing. It cheers him. He has been writing again lately."

"Writing now? A paralytic's poems from his arm-chair? That would be like his conceit."

"It seems to be prose this time."

"That's liker his conceit than ever. He can't write prose."

"That's unjust, George. You haven't read his pieces."

"Have you?"

"A few of them. I may not be a good judge, but I like them. He writes of whatever interests him, and that seems to me the best way to interest his readers."

"He's made a partizan of you, I see. He does of all the women."

"Isn't it natural he should, having no woman of his own?"

"It's wise. He gets himself taken care of. But then he always did that."

"You wouldn't stand it if anybody else said a word against him, George."

"Well, he is my brother. I suppose I'd better go up and see him now. It's only decent."

"That's right. Go now, before your mind has time to change. And try to be as pleasant as you can."

"I'll be civil. I'm sorry for the poor old fellow. But I hope he won't ask me to read any of his silly pieces."

"Don't worry, George. He won't."

XXXIX

1876

LOU WHITMAN, HORACE TRAUBEL

It is about dusk of a fine summer evening. Mrs. George Whitman, in a black dress that suggests mourning, is walking alone under the trees in front of her house in Camden. A young man who carries a large bunch of rather faded wild-flowers starts to turn in at the gate, hesitates, and then decides to approach her.

"Mrs. Whitman, my name is Traubel. I'm a friend of Walt's."

"I think I have seen you somewhere, haven't I?"

"Perhaps you have seen me talking to him under these very trees. I have sat beneath them so often that I don't feel a stranger here, even today."

"Brother Walt isn't here this evening."

"Has he gone back to Timber Creek?"

"Not to Timber Creek. Not tonight."

"I had hoped that he might. I miss him from Camden. But he benefited when he went out to stay with his friends in the country."

"He enjoyed a quiet and an independence that he can't have in Camden."

[243]

"He enjoyed more than that, Mrs. Whitman. The air and sunlight and solitude would have done him good in any case. But at Timber Creek he seemed to get close to inanimate Nature in a very singular way. Up to now his interest had always lain with people."

"I trust he may go back to Timber Creek later in the summer. His friends there will be glad to have him. But he will not go for a week at least."

"His grief keeps him here. I beg your pardon if I intrude, Mrs. Whitman. But the little boy, his name-sake, was very dear to Walt."

"I speak of those things with Walt. You will understand when I say I can't speak of them with everybody."

"Indeed I do understand. Walt is that way. With him you are never afraid of being thought mawkish or sentimental. The real you comes through."

"It does. The real you. The real me."

"These flowers, for instance—"

"You meant them for Walt. Let me put them in water until he comes. He went out just to be alone for a time. I'm not sure when he will return."

"If you will take them— Thank you. I'm not sure, though, that water will do them much good."

"They are a little wilted. But perhaps they will freshen."

"They are badly wilted, Mrs. Whitman. But that is a part of the story. They were gathered in the woods by an old negro woman who spent the day trying to sell them. At nightfall she was starting back across the river without having sold a single blossom. I bought them for Walt."

"I shall see that he gets them. Perhaps they will be

a kind of consolation to him. He was very fond of—
my little Walter—"

"I know. I know."

"I don't intend to give way. I want to tell you. All
this morning the little dead boy lay surrounded by fresh
flowers, and Walt sat in his chair in the next room. All
the rest of the children were about."

"Walt's nieces and nephews. He thinks so much of
them."

"They moved restlessly about, as children will. They
were impressed and bewildered. Finally the smallest
of them all, a tiny girl, went from little Walter to
Uncle Walt, and stood looking up mutely in his face."

"And what did Walt say to her? What did he say as
he picked her up?"

"How did you know he picked her up?"

"He would, I know."

"He took her on his knee, and said, 'You don't know
what it is, do you, dear? Neither do we. Neither
do we.' "

XL

1877

HERBERT GILCHRIST, WALT WHITMAN

The prim parlor in George Whitman's house serves sometimes as a shrine for pilgrims. Today the young English visitor is kept waiting for ten minutes. He is rewarded by the entrance of a man who looks older than his fifty-eight years warrant, and leans heavily on a stick. Yet the old man is magnetic as in his youth, and ripened from wilfulness into serenity. It is Walt Whitman perfected for posterity.

"You will excuse me if I don't greet you by name, young sir. The servant-girl forgot your name on the way upstairs."

"I told her to say I would come up to your room, Mr. Whitman. I had no desire to make you come down."

"I prefer to come down to visitors. It gives me a change of scene as well as of company. You would be surprised, perhaps, to know how many visitors I have. Some of them come in casually to see the old gentleman who sits so much in the window or limps about the streets and greets every one. Others come on purpose to visit the poet whose work they admire. Many of my strongest supporters come from England. You yourself are English, by your speech."

"I am English."

"A good many of my books have lately been ordered from England. Last year I brought out a new edition in two volumes, including my prose. I call the additional volume 'Two Rivulets.' The title symbolizes two flowing chains of prose and verse, emanating the real and ideal."

"I didn't know that you wrote prose."

"My prose is mere stray jottings from a life—my life—and notes that may illustrate my poems. The poems might do just as well without the footnotes. But a man must do something when he is laid by the leg."

"But, Mr. Whitman, you are a good deal better off than I had been given to understand. As you sit there you look quite hale and hearty."

"There are two years, or perhaps three, that I don't like to look back on. But I think Fate did its worst for me all at once. Things have been going better since."

"I'm glad to hear that."

"But I'm growing garrulous as I grow old. I spend so many hours alone that an audience starts me to talking. I've told you my history, undertakings, and prospects. You haven't even told me your name."

"My name is Gilchrist."

"Not the son of my correspondent, Mrs. Anne Gilchrist?"

"Say rather the son of Gilchrist's 'Life of Blake.' I am a painter by profession. But I'm known to the world only because at his death my father left a book unfinished, and my mother completed it."

"That should be your boast rather than your grudge. A young widow, left with an unfinished book and little children, might well have given way to despair."

"My mother is a remarkable woman. I acknowledge that, Mr. Whitman."

"You must pardon me if I speak warmly on the subject. For me your mother is one of the elect. When my book, 'Leaves of Grass,' was received with derision and abuse, she brought out in print 'A Woman's Defense of Walt Whitman.' I count it one of my greatest blessings to have inspired such a tribute from a woman and a mother."

"She was much taken up with your book. For years, it seems to me, she read nothing else, thought and talked of nothing else."

"You mean I was made a bugbear to the Gilchrist children?"

"We did hear a good deal of you. We used to mutter to each other that you were even worse than William Blake."

"You say you are a painter. Then perhaps it is hard for you to understand the literary temperament. You can scarcely realize what your mother meant to me. During years of neglect and opprobrium she never faltered in her enthusiasm and faith. Often she used to write to me every month."

"I can remember the evenings when she wrote to you, Mr. Whitman. Her days were full, often with what was really servants' work. There were four of us children, you see, and we were so beastly poor. But then sometimes after tea she would reward herself. She would sit down under the lamp with her paper before her and 'Leaves of Grass' open on her lap. As she wrote her face would shine like a devotee's. No matter how much noise we made, she never even heard us."

"Ah, those letters of Anne Gilchrist's! I have them somewhere now, her beautiful letters."

"You didn't always answer them very promptly."

"I sometimes didn't answer them at all. But that was at her own desire. If I received a letter from her, she arranged that I was to mail her a newspaper, just to show that her letter had reached me. But I always sent her my later poems as they appeared in magazines. I felt sure of her interest."

"You interested her. There is no doubt of that."

"You speak coldly, Herbert. Isn't your name Herbert?"

"Yes. Did you hear it so often that you remember it?"

"Not half so often as you heard mine, I suppose. Your mother made a hobby of me. You grew weary of your mother's hobby."

"I hated the very sound of your name, Mr. Whitman. But if I sit here now and stare at you, it isn't altogether because I'm sulky. It's principally because I like to stare at you."

"The old phiz has its attraction for painter chaps. And it has been photographed until the very cameras shriek."

"No photograph could do you justice. I suppose you wouldn't consider letting a beginner like me paint you?"

"Surely you wouldn't want to paint me: the old bore, the darned old humbug!"

"Laugh if you want to, Mr. Whitman. The joke is on me. But when you get through talking turn your face a little more to the light. That's it."

"Keep my face turned and stop talking, eh?"

"No. Go on talking while I get a pencil-sketch. Lord, what hands! A pencil can't do 'em."

"Did you come to America to paint?"

"Did I—did I what? Don't move your hands if you can help it."

"I thought perhaps you came to America to paint. Did you come over to fill an order for a picture?"

"No such luck. I was brought."

"You were brought to this country?"

"I was brought, along with the other impediments. Percy, my oldest brother, is married and rooted in England. But the rest of us came with the household goods."

"You mean your mother is in America?"

"To be sure she is. Lock, stock, and barrel. And the cat. And the canary."

"But in the name of heaven, why? That is, it's natural enough for an English author to come to America."

"So much white would be hard to paint. But, Lord, what a picture, if I could get it!"

"Listen, Herbert. I wrote your mother advising her against this very step. Three years ago when she first heard of my illness it appealed to her womanly sympathy. She wanted to rush over here to take care of me. But her generous course was out of the question.

I had care enough, and she had her own responsibilities."

"Don't let it vex you, Mr. Whitman. With that face, it must have happened to you before."

"What must have happened?"

"Fool women must have flung themselves at your head."

"But your mother is by no means a fool. She is a woman of brains and character."

"That makes it all the worse, Mr. Whitman. Because she's clean daft over you. She has never even seen you. Yet she vows you have revealed to her all that a woman may feel for a man."

"I owe her so much for her loyal support. I mustn't forget what I owe her. But, Herbert, do you think she wants to marry me?"

"Of course she does. She wants just that."

"How ghastly! My poor friend!"

"After all, you might do worse than let her marry you. She runs a household beautifully; she can produce domestic comfort on very nearly no money at all. Then she understands the business side of the literary life. She could write your letters for you, and interview editors. I believe if you married her it would double the sale of your books."

"But if I married her, I'd be married to her, don't you see?"

"The idea strikes you with panic, sir?"

"No doubt my panic is foolish. I've had everything else in my life. Why shouldn't I have a wife at last, and a comfortable home?"

"I think you will have, sir. I know my mother."

"Yet even now marriage would interfere with one

or two cherished plans. As soon as I can save a little money I had hoped to travel in the West, to review the great basin of the Mississippi, and see the Rocky Mountains for the first time. But if I were to marry now——"

"If you marry my mother, you won't go West or anywhere else unless she thinks it's good for you."

"But for fifty years I have been the only judge of what was good for me."

"Settle it as you must, Mr. Whitman. Naturally, I think the wise course for her is to go back to England."

"You think she can be persuaded to do that?"

"She can't be persuaded. But she might be forced. It's all very well to save her admiring letters. But if you were married to Mother you couldn't shut her away in a drawer. The only salvation for you is in flight."

"But I don't want to flee."

"I don't mean literal flight. I mean turn all the Gilchrists out and lock the door against them. Only don't do it just yet."

"You think I ought at least to see your mother and thank her for her long friendship?"

"No. I just don't want you to turn the family out until I've finished a picture of you. You've no idea what a hard subject you are, with all that white hair and beard. But, God, you're glorious!"

XLI

1878

ANNE GILCHRIST, WALT WHITMAN

Mrs. Gilchrist's lodging in Phila-
delphia. Mrs. Gilchrist is a stately,
middle-aged woman, who has sub-
sisted spiritually for years on what
she now begins to fear is an illusion.
In her makeshift lodgings she has
created a cozy domestic interior,
where she sits waiting by a bright
coal-fire. Six o'clock brings Walt
Whitman, with a powdering of snow
on his wide-brimmed hat and his shirt
open at the neck as usual.

"Sit down, Walt. Your chair is waiting for you."

"Ah, the wide, strong chair! It gives a man a welcome. A welcome, too, the bright coal-fire, and the
hearty English tea-table. And a welcome the very hour
of the day. It is a good hour this, between six and
seven, in many lives a holy hour, an hour of fulfilment.
It is the hour of the man who returns from work and
ceases to be merely the creature of his work, becomes
again the husband, father. It is the hour of the family,
the table, the story, love, frolic. An hour precious, ines-
timable."

"I confess I had expected you a little sooner."

"I set out early. My writing hours were over by noon. Then came the dinner my good sister Lou provides so carefully. Soon after that I took my stick and set out for the ferry. This is the same stick Peter Doyle gave me in Washington when illness first seized me. He nursed me then. A rough, uncultured fellow Peter is. But a better nurse no man could ask."

"Let me put your stick in the corner. You won't need it here. Did something detain you on your way to the ferry?"

"The ferry itself detained me, the ferry that should have sped me on."

"I shouldn't have thought the ferry rich in excitement in winter."

"In winter it is most exciting. To stand on the deck of a powerful boat, especially at night, and feel it crush its way proudly and resistlessly through the thick, marbly, glistening ice—there is strength, beauty, superbity."

"It got you here somehow, ice or no ice."

"Have you no feeling for boats, my friend?"

"The ocean-going ships are beautiful. But I see no cause for ecstasy in the Philadelphia-Camden ferry."

"The ferry-boats are beautiful too, and different one from another. The *Beverly* is the best of all, though the *Wenonah* is good too. My friend Ed Lindell, the gateman on the Camden side, tells me that the *Pennsylvania* is best of all in obeying her rudder."

"You have made a friend of the gateman?"

"He is a warm admirer of my books, tells me that he reads them over and over, though he reads nothing else. But in our talks we run mostly to boats and people. Many a vivid yarn have I picked up from Ed Lindell."

"The day I went with Herbert to call on you in Camden we crossed on a boat named the *Delaware*."

"How like you, Anne Gilchrist, to say a word in praise of the *Delaware!* But for you, the poor old *Delaware* might go unpraised."

"I happened to notice the name of the boat. It is an American name."

"But it is not the boats alone that make up the charm of the ferry. There are the great freight-houses, with their bags, bales, casks of merchandise. A drove of cattle will come to embark, and then a pressure of vehicles."

"That sounds like good Walt Whitman. You notice everything."

"And then the reception-room for passengers waiting—what scenes that presents! Business bargains, flirting, love-making, understandings, proposals. There is a porter, not quite right in all ways, who insists on sweeping up in the faces of the crowds. And in the midst of everything stands a great iron stove heated red-hot."

"I remember that stove."

"Today there had been a matinée performance at the theater here in Philadelphia. I ran into the stream of homeward-bound ladies. I never in my life saw a gayer scene. Scores of handsome, well-dressed Jersey women and girls, with eyes bright and cheeks glowing from the cold, a sprinkling of snow on their bonnets and dresses. They came streaming in for nearly an hour."

"While you sat and watched them?"

"I kept intending to move on. But it interested me to see that women can have capital times among themselves, with plenty of wit, lunches, jovial abandon. Doubtless, though, this is an old story to you?"

"I know nothing of it at first hand. I have never experienced jovial abandon in the presence of other women."

"Of course not. Why should you? What are ordinary feminine distractions to Mrs. Gilchrist the biographer of Blake, the friend of Rossetti and Carlyle?"

"Say Mrs. Gilchrist who waits tea for Walt Whitman. That is as steady an employment as any."

"You smile, my friend, but you hit shrewdly. Another time—"

"You will try to be prompter?"

"Another time don't wait for old Walt. He is off somewhere idling his time away, the old scamp, the old procrastinator. Trust neither his professions nor his punctuality."

"A certain casualness becomes you, Walt. And when you do arrive, your presence is a compulsion."

"Your patience shames me, as it has often shamed me before."

"We will have tea now. The kettle boils, and everything else is ready."

"But the children, your Herbert and Beatrice? Are we not to wait for them?"

"They will not be here today. They are off about their own concerns."

"I miss them. Their bright faces, their young voices, their hopeful enterprise. And they complete you. The strong mother, guiding their maturity as she has guarded their childhood, is a beautiful picture."

"They have grown beyond the need of me. Herbert is busy with his painting. Beatrice thinks of nothing but hospitals and dispensaries, and her ambition to study medicine."

"Beatrice belongs among the forward-looking women. I expect to see woman take her place in the professions as in literature and art. She must show what are her innate potencies, powers, attributes. And soon now, soon."

"But is not motherhood precious above all? Shall we not set the ministering woman above the book such a woman might write?"

"It is important to have the books, if only because of what they reflect."

"But are not women by their very nature better fitted to understand and appreciate than to create? 'Leaves of Grass' says many things as a woman must feel them. It speaks to me like the voice of my own consciousness. But I could never have written 'Leaves of Grass.'"

"Your achievement was as great as the actual writing of the book. You saw clearly when almost everybody else was engaged in raising the dust."

"Ah, Walt, I shall never forget my first reading of 'Leaves of Grass!' William Rossetti put into my hands first his book of extracts and then the complete 'Leaves.'"

"Rossetti was one of my first and staunchest supporters. So much of my strongest, best support has come from your England, from the free and noble spirits there, Rossetti, Dowden, Symonds. They read my book, rallied to my defense, set me down as one of themselves, yet a little above, in advance of them."

"Yes. As I was saying, when I first read 'Leaves of Grass' it was not like reading at all. It was as if I had touched a hand that grasped mine, heard a voice that spoke directly to my heart, felt for the first time a love enveloping and secure."

"The book was meant for such readers as you."

"But in reading it I felt that I reached the man behind the book. I cannot yet believe that I was mistaken."

"You were not mistaken."

"Ah!"

"Your grasp on my work is so wonderful, so sure, so all around, so adequate. And then your noble printed defense of me, 'A Woman's Estimate of Walt Whitman.' No one could go farther, see clearer than that."

"Rossetti insisted that it be published anonymously. I would willingly have shouted it from the house-tops."

"Rossetti's was the wise course, serene and cautious. We have so far to go that we can afford to go slowly."

"I may have been hasty in my defense, immodest, unwomanly."

"Say rather womanly in the truest sense. Courageous, passionate and godlike, not skulking behind the minor conventions and reticences."

"You forgive me my printed 'Estimate.' You have never forgiven my coming to America."

"It is not a question of forgiveness."

"The offense was beyond pardon?"

"Let me be honest. When you wrote and suggested coming I shrank at first. You had created a Walt Whitman who meant much to you. I felt you would be happier if your creation were not tarnished by the view of an old man going limping to his grave."

"I have found an old man, indeed. But do you think I am disappointed?"

"An old man and a natural lone-hander."

"Then the lonely old man goes to my heart, to be nourished, succoured, sustained there."

"You do, you do sustain me. The sight and thought of you erect among your children, the guiding, cherishing mother, gives me warmth about my heart, gives me faith in men and women."

"It's almost as good as the Camden ferry, perhaps?"

"The best of you has never got into your writing, Mrs. Gilchrist. In your talk around your tea-table the best of you has showed, freely poured forth to your own private circle."

"The best of me has never showed at all. It has been driven back into my own heart."

"I hope I haven't said anything to hurt you, my friend."

"You haven't said anything much. There, never mind! I ought to tell you, I am going to New York later in the winter. Herbert thinks it will be a good place for his painting."

"New York may suit him, but only if he is ripe for it. New York is a good market for the harvest but a bad place for farming."

"Didn't you like it when you lived there?"

"It is one of my cities of romance. In the prime of life the great cities draw us. To rest his worn-out body and spirit a man goes back to the country."

"In the country, surely, one gets closest to Nature."

"Ah, close, close, but not closest! Nature is there too in the crowded streets, the teeming wharves, the packed ranks of dwellings, the scramble and frenzy of the market-place. New York, Washington, New Orleans, were for me the cities of things begun. Camden is the city of things finished."

"But have you never thought of leaving Camden?"

"I think rather of putting up a little shack on a cheap lot, and burrowing in there for the rest of my days. I have the lot already, in a workingman's street where children abound in the gutters and stray hens cross the sidewalk."

"And you would live there alone?"

"Such a plan sounds droll, doesn't it, for me who have always drawn from the crowd my sustainment and vitality?"

"It sounds very lonely."

"Old age is lonely. To be sure, if I had married at the usual age I should not now be planning a hermitage for my last days. But then, if I had married at the usual age, there would have been no 'Leaves of Grass.' "

"Walt, will you tell me something, here in the quiet of this sacred hour? Was there some compelling reason why you did not marry at the usual age, why you have never married?"

"Hush, my good friend! I do not speak of that to anybody. To you I could if to anybody, my best, warmest, closest of friends."

"Thank you. I quite understand. Yet it seems like giving up the substance for the shadow, to go on as you are going."

"You are right, Anne Gilchrist. It is a waste and a weariness."

"An unnecessary waste."

"A waste I grant. Yet perhaps it has its own ends to subserve, and will subserve them well."

"But your face dulls in spite of you. For the first time in my sight you look like an old, old man."

"Think of me as an old man, a cussed old man, an old man driven by his uneasy spirit from the warmth and solace you so ungrudgingly offer. But he half wishes he could accept that solace, Anne Gilchrist."

"And only half wishes he could. Mayn't I give you something to eat? You are making a poor tea."

"Reach me my cane, please. I'm going now."

"But Herbert and Beatrice will be disappointed if they don't find you here when they come back."

"I shall return another day. We shall find much to talk about. There's that question of the size of books, for instance. I meant to go into that with you. But it must wait."

"Just a minute, Walt, if you're actually going. I'll ring for the landlady's son to walk down to the car with you."

"It isn't necessary."

"I've rung. Now wait. I don't like to have you alone in the icy winter streets at night. Or at any rate, not tonight."

XLII

1879

EDWARD CARPENTER, WALT WHITMAN

In George Whitman's parlor, Walt receives another of his English visitors. This is an earnest young man of the intellectual-and-radical stamp, with the Oxford hallmark.

"Here we are in the good arm-chair. Will you sit down yonder? That's right."

"I sent up my name, Mr. Whitman, though I wasn't sure it would mean anything to you. I didn't wish to intrude, if you were not well enough to see casual visitors."

"Do you call yourself a casual visitor, who cross the Atlantic on purpose to see these States? Or casual to me after your good letters? Too many of your letters went unanswered, but every one brought me the feeling of appreciation, of comradeship."

"You must get many letters from admirers of your work."

"Oddly enough, most of them come from England. I have found many friends in England, strangely yet most naturally. William Rossetti's Selections started the good work. Then my two-volume edition of three years ago sold best in England."

[265]

"I am proud that I was a subscriber to that edition."

"Ah, those blessed gales from the British Isles saved me! I was low then in pocket and in spirit. I have my up and downs still, but manage not to get so low any more."

"Your English readers, Mr. Whitman, look on themselves as your friends."

"I, too, look on them in that light. One of the staunchest of them is a woman. I allude to a Mrs. Gilchrist. Perhaps you know her."

"I do know an old lady of that name."

"An old lady?"

"I beg your pardon for the adjective. The lady isn't really old. But she runs a whole colony of children and in-laws, and I think a grandchild or two as well."

"You complete the picture for me. The culture, refinement, scholarship, the books and articles, are strengthened, vitalized, warmed by the gracious ministering motherhood. It was in such an aspect that I saw her while she lived in America. But she has gone back to England now."

"It's the same person, I've no doubt. Didn't she write a Life of Blake?"

"Not a Life, but *the* Life. Her book gathers together little things ordinarily forgotten, portrays the man as he walked, talked, worked, in his simple capacity as a human being. It is in just such touches, such significant details, that the art of biographical narrative lies."

"No doubt it is interesting from a biographer's point of view. Yet those very details that you call significant hampered Blake's genius and drove him mad. The high-born spirit is not fed by petty annoyances."

"Doesn't it find its own food, sometimes perhaps in strange places?"

"It should not be forced to. We must look to a re-distribution of material circumstances to free the great spirits which we in our turn are hampering."

"Salvation cannot be legislated, Mr. Carpenter. We must look farther than an Act of Congress for the creation of a great new literature."

"There is much to be done before we can even think about literature."

"What else is there that is worth our thought? A new superb democratic literature, and a generation growing up in perfect health, awake to all the instincts, desires, needs of the body, yet keeping the body well in rein—what more can we ask of the future?"

"I ask much more of it. But then I am a socialist. Perhaps you object to socialism, Mr. Whitman?"

"I do not object to socialism so much as to being talked to about it."

"That sounds as if others of the brotherhood had been at you."

"Aye, every *ist* and *ism* that the day affords. They seem to feel that I keep a foundling-home for un-fathered ideas. They come here to read me private lectures, interrupt the routine of the placid household, consider me a traitor because I will not come down and fidget with them."

"Their eagerness for support misleads them. Yet you might well have a certain sympathy for their isolation. Criticism has isolated you here in America."

"True, true. But would it not be just as true to say I have isolated myself? I don't think a man has any call to go out breaking heads and then expect the people he attacks to bless him for it."

"A new idea is always distrusted, Mr. Whitman, a new and original writer received coldly. Yet Mr. William Rossetti gave me to understand you had endured worse than that. He implied a cabal working against you in editorial offices, a systematic neglect that amounts to persecution."

"I am more used to being kicked out than to being asked in, if that is what you mean. Against editors, indeed, I might well cherish a grudge."

"So might others of us."

"But perhaps it is best not to have a royal road. It stiffens a fellow up to be told all around that he is not wanted, that his room is better than his company, that he has a good heart, that he can nurse soldiers but he can't write poetry."

"But for a man who has given his life to his poems, that is the worst kind of abuse. Why should you try to be serene under it? It shouldn't be endured at all."

"It should be contradicted, perhaps. But I can best contradict it in my own way. When another man says no, it does not seem to me that I can say yes. I can live yes. But I can hardly put my confidence in myself into blatant affirmations."

"Just the same the thing needs doing. Your friends should do it for you."

"Perhaps my friends are too busy being my friends to allow them time to explicate me to my enemies. Explications do not explicate. Certain people are eligible to understand me, will understand me anyhow. Certain other people are not to be reached. No sort of plea, no figures quoted, even, would affect them, would reduce the quality, quantity, vehemence of their prejudice."

"As you say that, it sounds convincing. Yet why should a man be distracted by swarms of gnats when he has a great work to perform in the world?"

"You speak like a man who has found his own work. Yet I have gathered from your letters that you were going through certain preliminary shufflings and doubts. Your endeavors must have set you on the right road at last."

"My work in this world, Mr. Whitman, is what any thinking man's work must be."

"And what is that?"

"To contemplate the ideal, and slowly translate it into life and action. That is the only good which I can see. And, after all, it is sufficient."

"It is a brave program. But the means, lad, the means?"

"In my own case?"

"In your specific individual case. Let us consider the case of Edward Carpenter."

"Very well, if we must. As I think I wrote you, when I left the University I decided to meet life on the lowest terms. I wished to go back to the land. With a college friend, a lad you would love, I looked around for a farm we could buy. You in America would not believe our difficulties in finding a freehold. All our good English soil is in the hands of hereditary landowners."

"What happened after you had found your farm?"

"We had still greater difficulties in making a living out of it."

"But you persevered, stuck to it, made it yield you your bread?"

"I began to doubt the righteousness of getting my

bread in that way. It was bread taken from the mouth of the agricultural laborer. A chance was offered me at a lectureship: to go out on money paid by the University of Oxford, and try to bring some intellectual light to the laboring man."

"A noble idea on the face of it, but I should think doomed to failure. You were trying to work from the outside in."

"It was discouraging work, certainly. In such a slough one man's efforts are swallowed, his life goes for nothing."

"Ah, that feeling of the writing person that he must make his life count! I sit upstairs here in my comfortable bedroom, cared for, waited on, solicitously served by my friends. Yet I am happy only because of the little pieces that I write and get published, happiest in watching the heap grow from month to month, so that I may some day make a book of the little pieces."

"You are writing again since your illness? That should be good news to your admirers."

"Aye, lad, I am getting together a new book of prose pieces, though it is yet far from complete. And I am once more revising 'Leaves of Grass' for a new edition. Two more throws against oblivion."

"But that is splendid!"

"It may be splendid. It is surely comical, the satisfaction, the sense of accomplishment, that comes from scratching with a pen on paper. A man makes a pair of shoes, the best. He expects nothing of it. He knows they will wear out: that is the end of the good shoe, the good man. Any kind of scribbler writes any kind of poem and expects it to last forever."

"It's the only thing that has any chance of lasting."

"That is both true and fundamental. I wish I could get our American young men to see it as you do, our handsome, intelligent young men of sound stock, eager to do the best they can with their individual lives, but allowing themselves to be carried off in the whirlpool."

"They cannot all write poetry. Doubtless they are needed in many places."

"But in no other so crucially. America has accomplished the greatest results in all features of modern life except literature, which is the greatest, noblest, divinest of all. There she is simply an absorber, an automatic listener, with no eye, ear, arm, heart of her own."

"Yet surely to listen well is a benefit."

"To listen well is an accomplishment. It is almost a trade in itself. But it is a trade I fear Walt Whitman never learned. Shut the old man up now, by force if necessary. Tell me of the good friends in England, the great writing chaps, the pyramids and colossi."

"William Rossetti is well, and ever your ardent champion."

"Rossetti is a man whose good will always turns to good deeds. Robert Buchanan, too, has been active on my behalf. My American friends have resented his published statements that I was in need. But his statements helped my sales in England, so I felt that neither America nor I was dishonored by them."

"Carlyle continues to live in Chelsea, in deepening despondence since his wife died. There was always talk that they didn't get on well, but in his own way he must miss her."

"Carlyle wouldn't be a cheerful man to live with. He has a devouring mind like a great furnace, but the combustion somehow not perfect, leaving a deal of very black smoke to be blown about the neighborhood."

"Your speaking of smoke makes me think of Tennyson, who is fighting the introduction of a railroad on the Isle of Wight."

"That is interesting. I see his point, yet it would never occur to me to do such a thing. I personally do not object to the age of steam."

"You are a young man, Mr. Whitman, whatever your gray hair may insinuate. Perhaps that is one reason why you draw so many young people to you."

"Yes, lad, the young fellows come. And often, often, the old men go. They serve an apprenticeship with me while they are getting their roots well in the soil. Then they pass on, maybe become professional, adopt institutions, find that Walt Whitman will no longer do."

"Yet it must always make a difference to them that they have been with Walt Whitman. I know whereof I speak. Your poems changed my life for me, gave me a reason to go on and a direction to go in. It is my object now to keep on with the good work that you have started."

"Whatever that may be."

"Surely in my many readings I have gathered the object of your poems."

"But how if I have no object in writing? How if I just write?"

"In that case I am disappointed. But I can't help feeling that the object has got itself into the poems in spite of you."

"That's a brave word, lad. Stick to all brave words, and to all brave purposes. They cost more than the cheap ones. But they never cost more than they are worth."

"I think some one just looked in at the door. Was it a hint to me that I ought to go?"

"If you go now, come back another day. Now or any other day, take with you for yourself and for my good friends in England a word of greeting."

"The manly word of comradeship. May I take that to them?"

"And the warm human handclasp, comforting to me as nothing else is."

XLIII

1879

A SCHOOL-TEACHER, WALT WHITMAN

A public school in St. Louis. A gray-bearded man who leans heavily on a stout cane has been trying locked doors along the corridor. A spectacled, woman, still young but marked by the hand of renunciation she cannot come to terms with, emerges from a room and catches sight of him.

"Good-day. Were you looking for some one?"

"I was looking for almost any one. Have things hereabouts stopped running?"

"They always do on Saturday."

"Is today Saturday? Bless me, what a joke on the old man!"

"Won't you sit down and rest for a few minutes? If you will come in here I can give you a chair."

"Thank you. It is a very good chair, and adequate to my weight. So this is where you go about your gracious work of teaching children?"

"This is where I teach children, yes."

"Won't you go on with your work, whatever it may be? If you come here on Saturday, you must have work to do."

"I have nothing pressing to do. I come here Saturdays because I have nowhere else to go. You see I live in a boarding-house."

"That is a common doom. I have spent most of my own life in boarding-houses."

"You've lived in boarding-houses?"

"Does that surprise you?"

"Yes, it does. I had taken it for granted that you came here to the school to see your grandchild. Or that is—I mean—"

"Don't apologize, my dear, for paying me such a beautiful compliment. But as a matter of fact I come to see all the children."

"You like children as much as that?"

"Isn't it only natural to like them? The dear children! We begin life all over with them."

"You wouldn't find children such a treat if you earned your living trying to beat something into their heads."

"There are two ways of earning a living, my dear, as you will find out long before you reach my age. One is to grind along with your eyes on the track. The other is to keep the track by feeling with your foot, and lift up your eyes to the smiling heavens."

"The heavens don't smile much for such as me."

"May I tell you a story I sometimes tell the children as I go about among the schools? It's really a story for grown-ups, but the children who have heard it once always ask for it again."

"I'm grown-up enough. I was twenty-eight my last birthday. But you may tell it if you like. I'm listening."

"The story deals with two cats who went on a trip from home. We might say they went for a walk in the country, or we might say that they went downtown here in St. Louis."

"Please have them go for a walk in the country."

"Very well. They went for a walk in the country, and were gone all day. After nightfall they returned home to a third cat who was laid by the leg as I am and hadn't even a walking-stick. He asked what they had seen on the way. The first cat said, 'A deep blue sky, with clouds like puffs of cotton. Leaves that the frost had turned to rainbows. A little boy helping an old woman with a heavy basket. A mother calling her children to their simple supper. Lights beginning to show in farmhouses, and each yellow light the center of a home.'"

"And the other cat? What did he say?"

"He said, 'Leaves falling with every gust of wind. Ice beginning to freeze in the muddy ditches. Men dank with the smell of the stable coming into farmhouse kitchens with dung on their boots. A dead bird lying in a wheel-rut. Snakes in the roadside grass. And why should I have to walk, anyhow, when cats no better than I ride in carriages on down cushions.'"

"Oh, I wish you hadn't ever told that story to a lot of wriggling children!"

"Why not?"

"Because it must have been meant for me."

"It was meant for myself as much as any one, my dear. But aren't we all passengers on the same ship?"

"When I listen to you I've a queer feeling, as if I had known you a long time ago. Yet surely I've never seen you before. I should have remembered you."

"I am a visitor in St. Louis. My home is in the East. At present I am living with a brother, but I hope some day to buy or build a little shack of my own. Then the life of boarding-houses will be done with forever."

"Oh, I so hope you may get a home of your own! Do you believe that if a person wishes long enough and hard enough, the very wish in itself has some power?"

"Over the wisher at least it has power."

"Do you know, I'm glad you don't live here? You would find St. Louis commonplace. Yet I'm sorry, too. We may never see each other again."

"We have seen each other this once. That is the important thing."

"It is, indeed. You won't think me bold if I ask you for your name? I should like to remember it."

"My name is Whitman, Walt Whitman."

"You can't be the Walt Whitman who wrote the dreadful book!"

"Did you find it a dreadful book?"

"I haven't read it. I took good care not to. Now will you excuse me if I go on with my work? I have a great deal to finish before the end of the afternoon."

"I am used to people who know my name better than they relish it. But remember you did not shudder at your first sight of me. You thought I was grandfather to all the children."

"Mr. Whitman, I'm a woman, and a poor woman, and I dare say my opinion isn't worth much. But on a question of simple right and wrong I dare to trust my own conscience."

"You mustn't trust anybody else's conscience, on a matter simple or complicated."

"I know as well as the wisest could know it, that there are some influences which ought to be stamped out, not encouraged."

"If by 'some influences' you mean Walt Whitman, the critter has had to thrive with very little encouragement."

"I have heard you were honored by some men who should know better. I have heard it even of Emerson. But then Emerson took it back."

"Emerson never took anything back. It doesn't matter so much what you say of Walt Whitman. He's used to it. But I want you to respect Emerson. I saw him lately in Concord, a broken man, yet even in the breaking as beautiful as ever. Emerson's face always seemed to me so clean, as if God had just washed it off."

"God had need to wash it off, when it was turned to the encouragement of evil-doers."

"I won't keep you from your work, my dear. Thank you for letting me sit here to rest. A gracious deed may be remembered long after simple questions of right and wrong have ceased to seem quite so simple."

"You and your like may wish for that day. Good women must use their influence to see that it never comes."

"Good-day, my dear. I'm sorry."

"But I didn't mean to hurt your feelings. That isn't it at all. Oh, he's out of hearing! He must be a little deaf. Of course he's an old man. I should have remembered that when I was speaking to him. But suppose the ladies in the missionary society ever found out that I had spent an afternoon alone in the building with Walt Whitman!"

XLIV

PFAFF, WALT WHITMAN

Pfaff's new restaurant in Twenty-fourth Street, New York, on a fine fall morning. Pfaff can hardly believe his eyes when he sees who has just sat down at a table.

"Why, it looks like—it is—but it can't be!"

"Then it's his very substantial ghost."

"But, Mr. Whitman, I can't tell you what it's like to see you. Many and many's the time I've thought of you. But you haven't been to see me in years and years."

"I haven't been down to New York for a long time, Pfaff. Not since before the war."

"You always liked New York."

"My own New York, not only the New World's but the world's city! I resume with eagerness the streets and sights I knew so well, Broadway, the ferries, the west side of the city, the democratic Bowery. And then the crowd, bubbling and whirling like the waters about the city."

"People want to go faster all the time, Mr. Whitman. It's getting to be nothing but chase, chase, chase."

[281]

WALT

"Aye, they see life, and the excitement keeps them up."

"That sounds just like you. You still like to stroll about and look at everything."

"And develop a roaring appetite in the process. I haven't yet had breakfast, Pfaff."

"The waiter will bring you your breakfast. I'll order you a bottle of champagne."

"You're the best judge of champagne in America, if you're still as good as you used to be. But I don't commonly drink champagne with my breakfast."

"You don't commonly come into Pfaff's after an absence of twenty or thirty years. Here, boy, put a bottle of that private stock on ice, and bring me back the key. Now, Mr. Whitman, I'm going to sit down and have a good look at you."

"The years have left their traces."

"Not so bad as I thought, though. I heard you was a cripple, and blind and deaf and off your head. But you don't look much different, only older."

"I've had some bad years of late. But I now get about pretty freely again. I journeyed as far as the Rocky Mountains two years ago, and up into Canada last year. My lameness persists. But let me lean my cane in a corner and put my feet under a table, and I'm not so bad even now."

"Here comes your breakfast, Mr. Whitman. Now let's see if you can eat with the old appetite."

"Your crisp fried fish are just as good as they used to be in the old place on Broadway."

"Ah, you liked it in the old place on Broadway! You used to sit and smile and watch the crowd."

"It was a crowd worth watching, Pfaff. Do many of them still come here?"

"Not many. It's the passing of time."

"Some of them passed long ago. There was Fitzjames O'Brien, the greatest dandy of them all."

"It takes an Irishman to be a dandy, Mr. Whitman."

"O'Brien with his swagger and his underlying sweetness, and his famous story of the 'Diamond Lens.' O'Brien was killed in the war. What has become of Harry Stanley?"

"He kept coming in for a long time, getting shabbier and more morose. At last he stayed away altogether. He's dead now too."

"Poor gay Harry! Dead of poverty and drink, with his best work never done. John Brougham grew very prosperous, didn't he?"

"He wrote a lot of plays that everybody liked. He was associated with Dion Boucicault, and did better than Boucicault even. But Brougham died last year."

"I know poor Ned Wilkins has gone."

"He was always your stout defender, Mr. Whitman. He told me once that he found in your books the health that had been denied him. He held on for a long time with his lungs going. That poor thin little voice of his got weaker and weaker, but he never used it for any but brave words."

"I used sometimes to run into Ned at Ada Clare's house. What has become of the beautiful Ada?"

"She went on the stage, was quite successful for a time, then dropped out of sight. Better not ask what became of her."

"And Daisy Sheppard?"

"Married a rich man, and died as rich men's wives sometimes do. She should have starved along and let Pfaff give her credit."

"George Arnold died soon after the war, didn't he? I came across a book of his poems the other day in a second-hand bookstore. 'Drift,' it was called. It had an introduction by William Winter. Winter is in New York, isn't he? And still writing?"

"And still scolding. He comes in here sometimes, and if anybody wants to start him off all they have to do is to say 'Walt Whitman.' "

"Poor Winter! He makes himself miserable over other people's success. Thomas Wood is still painting, isn't he? Yesterday I saw three pictures of his that had been bought for the Metropolitan Museum. They were named respectively 'The Contraband,' 'The Recruit,' and 'The Veteran.' They interested me deeply."

"He still paints, I guess. But nowadays he's mostly President and Vice-President of things, American Society of this, National Academy of that."

"There are more deaths than one for an artist, eh, Pfaff? Their morning freshness was too soon scorched and dried. Yet talking of them with you brings back their warmth and wit. They had the cream while it lasted, even if they never got to the bottom of the glass."

"Glass makes me think our champagne should be ready. Not those glasses, boy, the big ones. So. Old Pfaff has not lost his skill in selecting champagne?"

"Pfaff's champagne is worthy of being drunk while we think of the friends who are gone."

"After the first glass, Mr. Whitman, you shall tell me all about yourself. But the first glass goes best in silence."

"In silence and in remembrance. So."

"So."

XLV

1885

THOMAS DONALDSON, WALT WHITMAN

Walt's ambition for a home of his own has resulted in the purchase of an ugly two-story house in a mean part of Camden. Outside this house, 328 Mickle Street, waits Thomas Donaldson, member of an almost official group of friends that is gathering about Walt in his later years. Up the street comes a cloud of dust, in the midst of which is presently made out Walt driving himself in the buggy which Donaldson raised a subscription to buy him. Beside Walt sits a rather frightened half-grown boy. Walt with difficulty reins in the horse in front of his house.

"Hello, Tom! Isn't he splendid?"

"Mr. Whitman, in the name of common sense, what's come over you?"

"I've been out for hours, enjoying the gift of my friends. We've driven seven times around Camden this morning. I take Bill Ducket here along for company."

"But where's Frank, the sorrel pony we gave you

[287]

with the buggy? He was used to bring driven by ladies.
He's a safe horse for you."

"Frank is sold."

"You sold Frank?"

"He was groggy in the knees and too slow. Did you
want a pair of cripples to drive out, Frank and myself?
This horse is a goer and delights me with his motion."

"Certainly. But he will dump you in a ditch some
day, and that will end you."

"All right. He won't have to do it but once, and it's
a quick end."

"It seems to me like a chance you have no right to
take."

"Well, d'ye see, Tom, like most of the other chances
I've taken in my life, it's not really so chancy as it
looks. I usually have the boy Bill Ducket in the buggy
with me, and when the horse gets beyond my control
Bill helps me pull on the lines."

"Let Bill take the horse back to the stable now.
You've had enough for today."

"Easy, Tom. That's right. Now I'm down. When I
get back from one day's ride I begin to plan the next.
I was getting lamer all the time. But now my goings
out are not bounded by my own lameness. I have ever
fresh scenes, fresh sights, constant change and delight,
thanks to the thoughtfulness of you and my other
friends."

"Riding ought to help you, provided that wild horse
doesn't kill you."

"Shan't we go in the house, Tom?"

"Let's sit down in these chairs on the sidewalk. It's
a pleasant day to stay outdoors. Anyhow, I'm afraid
of those people who keep house for you."

"They are unpleasant. I shall have to do something about that couple, or else take permanently to my buggy."

"It serves you right for taking in a couple. In every such firm there is certain to be one working member and one passenger. All you need, anyhow, is a woman, preferably some widow who can cook a little and won't bother you by trying to clean."

"I dare say even the perfect housekeeper will be found in time. Ten years ago I was an invalid, forgotten by all but a faithful few, and well on my way to becoming a pauper. Then gradually my health improved. My books began to sell. The Boston publishers were threatened with prosecution, which whipped up public interest enormously. The first Philadelphia edition sold out in one day. And last year I moved in here to my own house, a freeholder at last."

"You'd do better to sell this house. I renew my offer of a house in Philadelphia rent free, a good house with spacious grounds."

"It's a kind offer, Tom. But I've taken root here. There are lilacs in the back yard, and I'm very handy to the ferry. Did I mention that I now have a pass on the ferry, presented to me by the company? Of all the fruits of my fame, there is perhaps no other of which I can make such constant use."

"This house may be near the ferry. But it's too near some other things."

"You mean the guano factory over on the Philadelphia side? But you can't smell that unless the wind is just right."

"Or just wrong."

"I mean right. It may be superstition on my part,

Tom, but it seems to me that the wind never sets in that particular direction except when I have visitors I'd like to get rid of."

"It's no use talking to you, Mr. Whitman, once you've made up your mind. You write about the fluid soul, but you yourself are more rock than river."

"But not insensible to kindness, Tom. Not insensible, even if hard to lay kindness on."

"Well, after all, you're a poet. It's a queer way of life, as I just had an illustration. You're a standing wonder in a neighborhood like this. The neighbors know your business is 'poetry,' but they never see a van drawn up here to cart your product away. Then you have so many visitors, and such odd ones."

"Yes. For the neighbors this house and its visitors must be a free dime museum."

"Whenever I come here I'm aware of a head in every window, usually peeping from behind a curtain that has not been pushed aside. But today as I approached I saw some one frankly on watch, a bundle of dirt munching bread with sugar on it. From behind the bread and sugar an audible yell, 'Hurry, Mam! There's a fat man at Whitman's door.' "

"Did Mam hurry?"

"She did. She was fat herself, and had evidently been interrupted at the family washing. I stood with your door half open. Says Mam to the voice behind the bread and sugar, 'Jimmie, watch if he comes out.' "

" 'Watch if he comes out!' That's rich. Then I'm under suspicion of being an ogre?"

"I'm fat enough to be tempting, I'm sure. Your guests are seen to enter, but there seems to be some doubt whether they ever leave."

"That is really a new one, Tom. A good many things have been said about me from time to time, but I don't recall its being suggested that I lunched off a fat Tom Donaldson."

"Things have been said about you, Walt, in higher quarters than this slum where you choose to live. That brings me to the object of my visit today."

"Has your visit an object, Tom? That's too bad, on such a nice day."

"The editor of the *North American Review* is sending you a message through me. His columns are freely open to you if you wish to reply to Swinburne."

"Why should I reply to Swinburne? He was an early admirer of mine, but I fear he has weakened in his allegiance. That's his affair. If Swinburne had but a few grains of meaning in his music, wouldn't he be the greatest charmer of them all?"

"There's more meaning than music in his latest utterance."

"Is there, indeed? Will you reach me that ball of twine in the window behind you, Tom? I see my cat coming around the corner of the house. When she finds me out here she always wants her game."

"Let your cat wait. Haven't you seen what Swinburne had to say about you in the last number of the English *Fortnightly Review?*"

"Swinburne had something to say about me, did he? No, I haven't seen it."

"I brought the article with me on that chance. Listen and I'll give you a sample."

"I'm listening."

"This poet says of his brother poet, 'But Mr. Whitman's Eve is a drunken apple-woman sprawling in the slush and garbage of the gutter amid the rotten refuse of her overturned fruit-stall; but Mr. Whitman's Venus is a Hottentot wench under the influence of cantharides and adulterated rum.'"

"Swinburne printed that about me? Ain't he the damnedest simulacrum?"

"But what are you going to say in answer?"

"Nothing, Tom. Just nothing."

"Aren't you going to answer it at all?"

"Not at all. But just leave the article with me, won't you?"

"Take it. I'm glad to be rid of it. But I don't see what you want with it if you aren't going to answer."

"I want it for a good enough reason. There are two things I would rather have in my own hands than in the hands of my friends."

"What two things, if I may ask?"

"An unjust attack on me, Tom, and a loaded pistol."

XLVI

1887

MARY DAVIS, WALT WHITMAN

The front room upstairs in Walt's own house in Camden. The accumulations of a writer, the freedom of an old bachelor, and the short tether of a paralytic, have united to produce an indescribable confusion. Out of the sea of papers, books and miscellaneous litter rise three islands of order: a wood-burning stove which Walt loves to tend, a solid bed neatly made up, and a huge rocking-chair with a wolf-skin spread over the back for warmth and softness. In this chair sits the old poet, beautifully bathed and brushed, with his writing-pad on his knee. His housekeeper, Mrs. Mary Davis, the ideal achieved in a young, strong, comely Jersey widow, has just brought the mail upstairs.

"Your mail, Mr. Whitman."

"Good, Mary, good. I'm always pleased to see the mail."

"It's pretty thick this morning. Not that that says

there's anything in it. Letters from autograph hunters, most likely, or from cranks who want to force their opinions down your throat."

"They'd have a nice time forcing, wouldn't they? I wish 'em joy of their job. But a letter even from a crank interests for a moment, gives a fillip to the curiosity. And then, you see, it needn't be answered."

"No. You can always drop it on the floor."

"You don't like the way I keep my room, Mary. It seems to you an utterly indecent place, disorder added to disorder. But then you must remember whose room it is. Critics have said that very thing about 'Leaves of Grass.' They claim the author got mixed up at the start and was never put to order again."

"I'm sure, Mr. Whitman, it's your own business how you write your books. But I don't see how you ever find anything in this mess."

"I can always find anything I want. Sometimes I find things I'd forgotten I had, or perhaps never knew about. This room is full of lost and found."

"It would be much easier to find what you want if you'd let me fix things."

"I hate to see things after they are 'fixed.' You get everything out of place and call it in order."

"It's your house, Mr. Whitman. At least I can keep my kitchen tidy."

"I will straighten up the clutter one of these days. I'm not exactly in love with clutter. But I am more famous for procrastination than for anything else."

"It never does any good to argue with you. You take the words right out of a person's mouth."

"Say, rather, that you take the weak side of the argument, Mary. For instance, you guessed that my

letters this morning would all be from bores and autograph hunters."

"Well, aren't they?"

"Not one of them. This first letter is from Dr.
Bucke, in Canada."

"Dr. Bucke who wrote the book about you?"

"Ah, the noble, generous, friendly book! And
judicious, too, in its way. Doctor is always judicious. In
this letter, though, he is not concerned with my place
among the immortals. He is worrying about my
stomach."

"Your stomach, indeed! If Dr. Bucke has any fault
to find with the meals I get you, let him write it to me!"

"His complaint would be that the meals are too
good. He speaks of my 'indiscriminate eating.' "

"It's a funny thing if a lame man living alone should
be grudged a good dinner to cheer him up."

"You've hit it as usual. The cheerfulness, serenity,
sense of well-being that accompany a good dinner we
value more than the food. And shall continue to value
them, in spite of all the doctors tell us. Eh, Mary?"

"I hope the next letter makes better sense."

"The next letter is from William O'Connor."

"The fiery Irishman? I like him."

"Aye, the fiery Irishman, burning in pure flame when
his friend or his cause is touched. He flares up splen-
didly today. He writes that the only modern books
worth preserving are Goethe and 'Leaves of Grass.' "

"I'm surprised he put in Goethe."

"William is not judicial, and all the better if he isn't.
I like the hater, the lover, the unmistakable yes or
no. I like the street 'Damn you' or 'How are ye, my
boy?' "

"And you like one nearly as well as the other, seems to me."

"Then, there's a letter from John Burroughs."

"Does he ask you to come and live with him?"

"He asks me that periodically. But don't worry, Mary, I'm not going. Yet I am happy to think that John bought his farm up on the Hudson, and possesses his soul there."

"It's not much he'll bother himself with farming, when he can go through the country sticking names on the birds and the chipmunks."

"You wrong him, Mary. John is a singularly complete man. And I'm not going up to live with him, as I've told you before."

"He keeps right on asking you."

"That is all the letters today. But here is a pamphlet from England. A paragraph is devoted to 'Leaves of Grass.' See, it is marked in blue pencil."

"I suppose that pleases you."

"It shows the drift. They come and they come, the tributes, tokens, allusions. 'Leaves of Grass' is creeping, gliding, advancing into its own."

"The English can't have much to keep them in their own country. Leastways all they do is to come to America and knock at your door."

"Surely they haven't been annoying you this early in the morning."

"One came to the kitchen door before I'd had my breakfast. Had a glass stuck in one eye, same as most of them have. Said he came to America to see Walt Whitman and Niag'ra, same as most of them say."

"Did you tell him to come back later?"

"No need to tell him that. They all come back later."

"Use your own judgment about admitting them. The companion spirits I must see, if only for a few minutes. But keep out the impostors and the bores. The impostors might be endured, because they feed a certain curiosity. But keep out the bores, Mary, keep out the bores."

"Do you still hear from that young Englishman with the hard name! The one who painted your picture and gave you curly hair in it?"

"You mean Herbert Gilchrist. I had a hard time not hurting his feelings about that picture. He took it back to England with him. But Herbert is coming to America this very year. He got fifty guineas or so from his book about his mother."

"And the money is burning a hole in his pocket?"

"Herbert is a poor man, like most of those painter chaps. Not extremely poor, but enough to make fifty guineas look like a lot to him. I wish he could have made this money in some other way. I have never got over the shock of his mother's death two years ago."

"She thought a pile of you, Mrs. Gilchrist did. You've often talked to me about her."

"I've talked to many people about her. I wrote a poem in her memory, too, and had it printed. But sometimes I wish I had answered her letters oftener, had thought just a little more about her and less about the admiration with which she was always so generous."

"There's been a plenty of them, those admiring women. How about the English lady who sent you the knitted red vest not big enough for your canary?"

"Ah, Lady Mount Temple and her famous waistcoat! That is about here too, somewhere in the dis-

order. The Customs people charged me three dollars
and a half duty on that red waistcoat, and I could
never get it on even to say I had worn it once. I was
always a free trader on principle, and now more than
ever. Free trade makes for solidarity, Mary, and at
the same time defends us from aggression."

"I must get about my work now. I'd like to finish
early today, so I can sew on your new shirts. Will you
want the horse and buggy this afternoon?"

"Yes, the horse and buggy. It acts as legs for the
man whose own legs have gone back on him."

"It helps you to pass the time. You fill your days
pretty full, what with driving every afternoon, and
your writing in the morning, and those new books Mr.
Traubel is always bringing, and you lose in the litter
on the floor."

"And the much talking, Mary. Don't forget the
talking. I used to go out and move among men as one
of them. Now I sit here day after day, talking, talking, like a dictionary that has sprouted a beard and
got itself a mouth."

"It does a man good to talk, Mr. Whitman. Does
other people good to listen to you."

"Thank you, Mary. Thank you."

"Before I go I must have just one look at the lady
over the mantelpiece. I look at her every time I come
into the room."

"That old daguerreotype? You've noticed it?"

"No one who chanced to see it at all could help but
notice it. She has such a charming, winning face."

"Ah, do you think that?"

"Indeed, yes."

"She was a sweetheart of mine, a sweetheart many,

many years ago. Some day when I feel more like it I will tell you about her. But not now."

"Is she still living?"

"I don't know."

"St! I shouldn't have asked that. But if she is living you'll hear from her one of these days. She might even come to Camden to see you. Everybody seems to find the way here."

"She wouldn't ever do that. Yet I somehow can't believe that I've heard the last of her. While my life goes on she must go on. But I'll tell you more another time. And, Mary—"

"Yes?"

"If that fellow with the single eyeglass knocks at the door again, just let him come up. I'll see what I can make of him."

XLVII

1888

HORACE TRAUBEL, WALT WHITMAN

Walt's Camden bedroom, to which a fresh shock of paralysis has tied him closely. But there are new signs of active life: sheets of galley-proof, a stack of engraved portrait frontispieces, samples of binder's cloth, and penciled memoranda pinned to the table-cover, not to mention a large, highly polished apple hobnobbing on the table with a jar of autumn flowers. By the light of a gas-jet Walt is putting his autograph on a very handsome middle-aged photograph of himself, which is thus made ready for the eager hands of Horace Traubel, his disciple and Boswell. Traubel at thirty keeps much of the candor and affectionateness which first drew Walt's liking.

"There you have it, Horace. My phiz with my name and yours on it. Put it with the scraps you are always saving."

"You haven't turned up anything more today?"

"I haven't turned up anything today. Yet it has been on the whole a good day, writing, reading. After a bad interval the writing comes back first, then the reading."

"You surely are progressing now, Walt. I can see from day to day that you are definitely better."

"As much better as a man can be who is chained now to one room, fares only from the bed to the chair, is looked after by a nurse. It is a weariness, Horace, a weariness, but we mustn't complain. In the summer it looked as if we might be worse off than this."

"You gave us a rare scare in the summer."

"I thought myself it would be the end of the old man. One night, Horace, you were in here when things were at their worst, you and the doctor and Tom Harned. I talked a little daffy that night, realized it afterward. I think, though, that my mind will not go. The throne may reel, but it never gives way."

"At any rate, you are better now."

"After every setback I get better, but not so much better. The track is always downhill."

"This last seizure was brought on by your own carelessness. Or at least Dr. Bucke thinks so."

"Maurice Bucke thinks so, does he? Maurice was with us last summer at the Harneds'. It was a blessed day, Horace, the good talk, the old friends, the champagne. But after I took Maurice to the station I drove out into the country. That was what did the business for me. I sat for an hour watching the sunset and came home chilled. Then in the night I woke up with all manner of devils upon me."

"The sunset was scarcely worth what it cost you."

"Still, it was a very fine sunset. And it may be the last I shall ever see out in the free air, as a free man. You know the horse and buggy are to be sold?"

"I know Tom Harned wants you to sell them."

"Aye, Tom Harned your brother-in-law, the same Tom Harned who wanted me to make my will when things were at their worst. He had his way about the will. I dare say he will have his way about the horse."

"Tom Harned told my sister he found you ready enough to listen to advice, but you took your own time about falling in with it."

"Tom must just give me my time, then. I can't be hurried. Even in an extremity, no good can come of hurry. Well, let Tom go. Let the horse go. We have something better to busy ourselves with."

"You mean the new book?"

"I mean just that. Did you bring me any proof this evening?"

"Four galleys, and the beginning of the page-proof as well."

"Four galleys ought to about see us through."

"It does see us through. The new book is at last set up."

"All thanks to the printer. He has been patient with our delay, has understood our peculiar situation and needs. I thought I had a silver dollar in my pocket. Yes, here it is. Give this to the printer, Horace. Not to the boss, mind you, but to the fellow who actually did the work. Tell him to use it for his lunch tomorrow, to get some cheese and beer and eat and drink to the new book."

"Have you definitely decided on a title?"

"I have. After twenty trials, each written down

and duly weighed and considered, I hit at length on the title, 'November Boughs.' "

"I rather like the sound of that. It is suitable, too, for this late collection of prose."

"We were sure to get it right in the end. You know, Horace, I have a great faith in ends. We miss a lot as we go along, mix up bad and good and indifferent. So many of our attempts are hits in the dark. But the end is sure, the right end."

"Your speaking of ends makes me think of the page-proof. You see here in one of these first proofs a piece ends with the page. I know you don't like the look of that. I've heard you speak of such bad arrangements."

"Show me the place, Horace. Ah, that's easily settled! We'll simply cut out two sentences, and finish five lines short of the end of the page."

"Don't you think more than that of your lines, Walt?"

"Not so much as I think of the looks of the printed page. Here a little farther on there's another difficulty. Here's a blank space between two notes."

"You can close that up by shifting the pages."

"There's an easier way. I'll add a line instead. There, I think the printer can read my pencilings. That makes the page sightly and beautiful."

"You always know the easiest way out of printers' puzzles."

"Who should know it if not I? The love of print has shaped my whole life. If I had not begun as a printer, I might have lived 'Leaves of Grass' instead of writing it."

"The printing itself speaks to you, Walt, quite apart from what it may have to say?"

"The printed page has a character and physiognomy of its own, for good or evil. My idea of a good page is an open one, wide open: words broadly spaced, none huddled, lines with a grin. Some printed pages seem to have a hump in the back. There on the table you will find a new English magazine with beautiful printing."

"The magazine of the Hobby Horse Guild. Are you a subscriber, Walt?"

"Not a subscriber in any sense. That magazine is like a table set with fine china, costly lace, fresh napkins, finger-bowls, but no food. I do not object to the refinements as such. But they do not take the place of substance."

"Still, as you say, the printing is beautiful."

"English printing of the better sort is always a delight, Horace. It is the one thing that makes me wish I had been born in the old monarchical island. American printing is all gloss and glare, the paper bad, the ink anemic. It makes me think of the prettiness of drugstores, the polished bottles, the painful glitter."

"Yet you like polish in its place. Or so I judge by that splendid apple. Are you going to eat it for your supper?"

"I'm not going to eat it at all. I shall keep it to look at, partly for its beauty, partly for the sake of him who sent it to me."

"A new friend or an old one? You have many of both."

"One of the oldest. John Burroughs."

"Is John still making out well with his farm?"

"Not so well with the farm, but capitally with himself. He had to take some decided step. His wife, d'ye see, is one of these perfect housekeepers. Her constant cleaning would madden a man. She was always friendly to me, though. She should see me now in this room, eh, Horace?"

"But he hasn't got free of her?"

"To be sure he has."

"You mean he has left her?"

"No, John wouldn't do that. He's a gentle soul. And then, of course, there's the boy. But John found a real solution of a bad situation. Back in the woods on the remoter part of his farm he built a cabin, at first intending it for a study. Now he stays there nights as well as days. Mrs. Burroughs lives in the farmhouse and cleans it to her heart's content."

"That doesn't sound like an ideal arrangement."

"It wouldn't, to a young man with a girl like Anne Montgomerie. Anne hasn't been to see me lately. Tell her the old man misses her when she doesn't come."

"She will certainly come within a day or two. I promise that."

"Mind you, Horace, I don't expect her to be faithful as you are. Not a day have you missed since my illness. What I should have done without you I don't know. But your patience has been taxed, and your own affairs must have suffered."

"My affairs are not so important. A bookkeeper's job pays for daily bread, but gives no sustenance to the spirit. I've gained more from you than I can possibly have given."

"There can be no striking a balance in matters of affection. Let's pair off, Horace, and shake hands upon it."

"Thank you, Walt. It has been a long association,

hasn't it, since those days when you used to stroll out under the elms at your brother's house, and one day I stopped and spoke to you."

"I remember you very well as you were in those days, Horace. You were a mere boy then, so slim, so upright, so electrically buoyant. You were better than medicine to me. And how you used to talk twenty to the dozen, and all about your endless reading!"

"I must have bored you frightfully."

"You didn't even alarm me. I saw that you were safe among books, that you were going straight, not crooked."

"After all, Walt, a man is entitled to all the culture he can carry."

"And to all the affection he can command? I hope so, Horace. I hope so."

"And at the bidding of affection a man can do wonders."

"A Horace Traubel can. What's that memorandum pinned to the table-cover? I can make out your name even at this distance."

"It says, 'Binding for "November Boughs."' You must make up your mind soon about the binding."

"My mind is already made up. I will have it in the wine-colored cloth. That dark wine-color is a passion with me now. I must get it on something that belongs to me."

"Then we have all the details of the book settled?"

"Yes, and enough of the book for now. Yet I must not be ungrateful to the book. Work on it stimulates me, bears me up. I think that during these last dark months I should have died if I had not had the book to do. It is necessary to have an ambition, a purpose, something you must absolutely personally do."

"Dr. Bucke writes me not to let you work too hard on the book."

"You write back and tell Dr. Bucke that I long ago promised you not to die until the book is done. That should satisfy even Doctor."

"You always keep your promises, I know. But then you don't make many."

"Shrewdly noted, Horace. I hate the compulsion of a promise. Perhaps that is the real reason why I have never married. If I had ever designed to marry, I should have begged off when the day came."

"I think there is a deeper reason than that. You have hinted that some day you would tell me all about it."

"Not tonight, Horace. Not tonight. I'm going to lie down on the bed now."

"Let me help you."

"You can't help me. Just have patience with me. I'd sooner die helping myself than live being helped."

"There you are! You managed that very nicely."

"It was quite an achievement, Horace, for a man who used to walk ten or fifteen miles at a stretch. But how sweet the bed is, the dear bed! When a fellow is physically in the dumps, the bed gives him a sense of freedom."

"You look very comfortable and peaceful. Good Heavens!"

"What's the matter, Horace?"

"That awful noise! What can it be?"

"That? Just my neighbor next door chopping wood."

"But does he split his wood on the floor?"

"That's exactly what he does, and seems to get up in the middle of the night to do it. He's not a particular fellow. Often he takes a notion of early morning to get up and tramp steadily about his room, miles and miles. Then he makes his fire. Then he whistles."

"We shall put a stop to that. I wish you had spoken about it sooner. He has no right to wake you at all hours, or disturb you when you are trying to work."

"Oh, let it go, let it go! Perhaps it will be put down to my credit in the general bill. We have to settle all accounts, Horace. This account of bad health is none of the pleasantest. But it must be paid."

"You keep very cheerful over it."

"Usually, not always. Sometimes I get to wondering whether it's all on the square, and I get sore, resentful. Then there's the other matter of my acceptance by the world. There are days when I go on like any other scarifying quarreler because the world will not take me at my own value."

"But surely you don't keep on long in that strain?"

"Sooner or later I find my way back to my central thought, my spinal conviction. I resent my resentment, am ashamed of my questions. Besides, d'ye see, there's no need of taking myself by my suspenders and putting myself on a pedestal of my own erection. Maybe Walt Whitman's not ahead of the world, after all. Maybe the world's ahead of Walt Whitman."

"Suppose the whole damned thing went up in smoke, Walt. Would you consider your life a failure?"

"Not a bit of it. I don't think a man can be so easily wrecked. I have put up my life for what it was worth, pouring it into the book without stint, honestly giving the book all, all."

[309]

"If that was your ambition, you've fulfilled it nobly."

"God knows whether I've fulfilled it at all. Here I am about stepping out with the case still undecided."

"You remind me, Walt, of a poem by Béranger. It's about a poet who was all the time asking questions of Providence. He was told to 'Sing, poor little thing, sing, sing!' and ask no questions."

"That's mighty good, and mighty pat. Sing, Walt Whitman, sing, sing, and ask no questions!"

"Have you finished any proof for me to take back to the printer?"

"It's there on the table, in what I call Horace's corner. But you're not going yet?"

"I must go. I've tired you out."

"I've tired myself, Horace, but the result was worth it."

"We have had a good talk, haven't we?"

"A good talk, Horace. One of our best. We are growing nearer together all the time. The other things have a certain place and weight. But the best in life is, after all, just this. Just to grow near together."

XLVIII

1889

RALPH DETIENNE, WALT WHITMAN

Wrapped in a new blue dressing-gown, Walt sits in his bedroom, with his great rocking-chair drawn close to the stove. His hair and beard are now snow-white, his eyes the wintry blue of old age. At seventy he looks ninety, looks indeed as old as Time itself. But across the writing-pad on his knee his pencil moves steadily, slowly, with frequent alterations. At seventy as at thirty, life demands expression. A pilgrim, a fresh-faced, handsome lad with a strong Southern accent, is admitted by Walt's male nurse.

"I'm an admirer of your poetry, Mr. Whitman, and admitted on that account. But I'm in here on my good behavior. I've been warned not to stay too long or talk too much."

"Draw up a chair beside the stove, lad, and make yourself comfortable. My housekeeper and nurse issue warnings in order to square themselves with their consciences. I've had a good day today. Not what at your age I should have called a good day. But as my days go now, good, good."

"But I see you are writing. I don't wish to interrupt."

"I have finished for the present. I keep my writing-pad always within reach. When the fire flares up I write, read whatever is handy, see company. It is a good day. Every evening Horace Traubel comes, gathers the scraps, takes them away with him."

"You are planning still another book?"

"I plan nothing. I go on now from day to day. But if I am spared, a book will make itself. An old man's book, as 'Leaves of Grass' was a young man's. Yet, after all, a pendant, completion, last interpretation of 'Leaves of Grass.'"

"'Leaves of Grass' needs no interpretation, Mr. Whitman, not even yours."

"There speaks the voice of enthusiasm, grateful to an old writer's ears. Right, gloriously right so far as it goes; but it does not, cannot, go all the way."

"Perhaps what youth feels as poetry, old age thinks as prose."

"It should, lad, it should. I don't say a man's old age is as important as his youth, or his work as strong. That does not come in. I only say that in the larger view, in the scheme I originally laid down for the 'Leaves,' an attempt to put a Person freely, fully and truly on record,—in that scheme the last old age is as essential as the record of my first youth. It is essential even if the old age be the old age of a dotard."

"That's splendid, Mr. Whitman. I understand that in a sense your whole life is itself the book. But for

'Leaves of Grass' as it stands I have a peculiar reverence and affection."

"Whenever it touches your life directly 'Leaves of Grass' is your book, and you yourself to that extent its author."

"It is generous of you to say so. But I should like to tell you my experience with your book."

"Indeed I want to hear it. Won't you move your chair closer to the stove? It grows colder as darkness draws on."

"If you see me shiver, don't blame your fire. But ought there to be quite so much smoke? It makes my eyes smart."

"The stove-pipe sometimes slips out of its hole. If you call my nurse, he will fix it."

"He might also send me packing. Let me see what I can do by standing on a chair. There! It slips in quite easily."

"It must have been out for some time. The room is cold, now that I notice it. You manage the stove-pipe as if you were well used to the job."

"It's my maiden effort. Stoves haven't played a great part in my life. I spent last winter in Egypt, and I was brought up in New Orleans."

"I was in New Orleans myself thirty—no, it is forty years ago. I have never been there since. But it has always remained for me a city of romance."

"It is a city of iron-clad tradition."

"You belong to one of the traditional families, then, I should judge."

"One of the families that marry each other, live on in the old houses, worship by rote and draw their very breath according to tradition. All the cousins look alike, and they all look like New Orleans. To be sure, my own father was different. He had blue eyes and a ruddy skin. He refused to enlist in the war, and married to suit himself. He was his father's favorite, perhaps because he was the eldest son. But there was not the slightest likeness between him and the rest of the clan."

"You say 'was?' "

"My father and mother were both killed in a carriage accident when I was a little boy. They were mad about each other. I can't imagine either of them wishing to survive the other. But their death left me to be brought up by my grandmother. I spent many years alone with her in the house except for our black servants. She had had other children, but they all left her as soon as they could. My grandfather spent most of his time in Paris."

"You must have been good company for a lonely woman."

"On her good days she wouldn't leave me alone for a minute, and with me in tow she raged through that old house like a whirlwind. Then for a week at a time she wouldn't leave her bed. When she had one of those spells she wouldn't speak except in French, and unless we answered in French she would pretend not to understand us."

"You passed a lonely childhood?"

"Lonely, and as I see it now very strange. Then two years ago I fell madly in love."

"That was natural enough at your age."

"Like everything else in your 'city of romance,' my love went wrong. I lost my girl."

"You lost your girl, in New Orleans? A French girl?"

"It happens that she was French. I went to Egypt to forget her, and instead of forgetting sank into a dull despair. Then one day, turning over some old books of my father's that I had brought along for sentimental reasons, I came across a worn copy of 'Leaves of Grass.' "

"That would be an early edition. You didn't happen to notice which one?"

"No, because it hardly seemed to me like a book at all. Reading it was simply being born anew."

"That is a grateful word to an old man held prisoner by illness, but reaching out through his book to help and console."

"Any author may hope to do that much. But I can't find words to express how 'Leaves of Grass' lifted my burden, eased the strain, made me see that even my unhappy love had its place in the scheme of my life. When I returned to this country, I couldn't be satisfied until I had found you and thanked you."

"You remind me of an old Quaker lady who came yesterday to buy 'November Boughs.' It contains a piece about the Quaker Elias Hicks, whom I had heard in my childhood. She stayed only a minute, wouldn't sit down. But she left an envelope on the table with the words, 'Don't open this until I am gone. This is not for thee alone but for me.' The envelope contained a five-dollar gold-piece. It is not enough for us that a love exists. We are all made so that we want to express our love."

"I think I should like that old lady. You remind me

that even my virago of a grandmother softened once at the mention of your name."

"That is not so singular. Women have been the clearest understanders, staunchest upholders of my poems."

"She must have read them some time, though I never saw her open a book. She had been a great reader in her youth, I've heard."

"At any rate, she recognized my name?"

"One day when she was tearing away at me in her best style from her bed I turned on her and shouted, 'You listen to what Walt Whitman says.' Instead of listening she sat straight up in bed and forgot her French. She shrieked back at me, 'What do you know about Walt Whitman?' "

"Yes, yes?"

"I began to talk about your poetry, to tell what it had meant to me in that winter in Egypt. She fell back on her pillow. Presently without looking at me she said, 'I wonder whether he's still living?' "

"She didn't know?"

"I told her I had heard that you lived in the North, that you were growing in reputation, and many people came to see you. I couldn't be sure she was listening. But when I said that some day soon I intended to visit you myself, she snapped, 'You keep away from him! Keep away. Mind now what I'm telling you. Keep away!' "

"What is your grandmother's name?"

"Madame Detienne. I am Ralph Detienne. She was my father's mother, you see."

"No, no! I mean her own name."

"Her own name perished long ago, as she was an

only child. But of course I have heard it. It was Desmoulins. What's the matter, sir?"

"Nothing. I dropped my cane. A cane becomes second nature to an old man. Thank you, thank you. Is your grandmother a very beautiful woman?"

"She may have been at one time. Creoles fade early."

"She looked nothing like that lady over the mantel?"

"What a jolly old picture, that young beauty with the clustering ringlets! I suppose she, too, must be old by this time. The daguerreotype has faded."

"Aye. An old man's pictures fade, fade. Turn up the gas-jet for a moment, lad, and face me. That picture at least is bright enough. Your father must have looked much the same. How old are you?"

"Nineteen. But I'm generally considered to look twenty-one."

"And with something of Fernande about the mouth."

"How did you know Old Madame's name was Fernande? I suppose I must have mentioned it. But that's droll, because I had all but forgotten it myself. I never heard it except in a few business transactions. She has always been 'Old Madame' to me."

"Old—Madame—Detienne."

"Is that a step on the stair? I want to leave before I am turned out."

"It must be Horace Traubel. He is early tonight."

"Perhaps he wants something special. In any case, I mustn't stay longer."

"Don't wait even to meet him. Horace sometimes takes it upon himself to regulate my visitors. Come in, Horace, come in. My caller is just going."

[317]

XLIX

1889

HORACE TRAUBEL, WALT WHITMAN

*Young Detienne leaves Walt's bed-
room abruptly, but not before Horace
Traubel has had a look at him.*

"Was that some nephew I never met, Walt?"

"No. He was a stranger, a pilgrim."

"I thought he had a strong Whitman look about
him."

"He was quite a stranger. I never saw him before."

"I hope it will be quite a time before you see him
again. How upset you look, Walt! Let me help you to
the bed."

"Yes, help me tonight. Let me lean on you."

"There you are, safe and comfortable. We shall
have to do something to check your visitors. We can't
have you so upset."

"An old man's tears flow easily, Horace. But they
soon stop."

"Mrs. Davis said you'd been having a good day.
She thought you were writing most of the afternoon."

"I was writing, and I shall keep on writing. What
does it matter to me if she never looked at my books?
It was a book of mine that saved him. And his

father read and loved me, though he never guessed."

"Shall I turn down the gas, Walt?"

"Turn it down. And don't feel of my forehead again. I'm not feverish. The room is cold."

"It's turning cold outdoors. Yet I thought this morning that the buds on the lilacs were swelling."

"On my lilac too, Horace?"

"I didn't look at yours."

"You despise my lilac because it gets dusty. You see the dust. I see the lilac."

"You always will, Walt. Shall I take along these notes and sort them for a new book?"

"Who knows if there will ever be another book? The sands are running low at seventy."

"You've closed your affairs half a dozen times at least. Then things take a turn for the better, and you begin again to write."

"I'm a fool for my pains, Horace. The criticism of 'November Boughs' was of the 'pity the old man' order. I'd rather be damned outright."

"You knew yourself that it was the book of late autumn."

"Autumn is all right, Horace. Old age is all right. What daunts us is the fear that there isn't much to follow."

"You may feel daunted tonight. But tomorrow you will get a good paragraph out of the sands running low."

"I might even make a book out of it. 'Sands at Seventy' would be the title. Let 'em pity the old man if they must."

"So long as the old man doesn't pity himself, Walt."

"For a moment just now I was guilty of pitying myself. Simply because I am an old man. But I was young once. It is only living that has made me old. And old and young, I have had a great deal out of living."

"A great deal, Walt."

"Aye, Horace. More than you know. More than I can ever tell you. Even the things people have tried to keep from me, I have had in spite of them."

"Gently, Walt, gently. Don't excite yourself."

"Gently be damned! Who has a right to excite himself, if not old Walt Whitman? Over there behind the table you will find a big bottle in a straw case. Bring it to me."

"Is this it?"

"That's it. It's fine sherry. Tom Donaldson gave it to me."

"It hasn't been opened."

"You open it now, and get two glasses."

"Dr. Bucke has left orders that you aren't to have anything to drink."

"Aye, Maurice's orders! Maurice's orders have been pretty faithfully carried out. But there are times when even Maurice must be adjourned. You pour that sherry, Horace, if you don't want me to get off this bed and pour it myself."

"If you insist, I'll pour it. You want me to drink with you to 'Sands at Seventy'?"

"Let me sit up before you give me the glass. I want you to drink with me to the young lady over the mantel."

"Are you going to tell me about her some day?"

"There's nothing to tell. She left me once, but I've

always kept her with me. Now I know that I shall always keep her, until the sands run out altogether. She has kept me too, in spite of herself."

"Walt, you have the strangest eager look now, just like a young man's. Yet when I came into the room you were sitting here crying."

"Fill my glass, Horace, and then put the bottle away. I shall have to get a good start tomorrow if there is to be a new book. 'Sands at Seventy' it is. And let any one who dares, pity the old man!"

L

1892

HORACE TRAUBEL, WALT WHITMAN

Alien influences have been at work in the familiar bedroom. There is a trained-nurse tidiness about it now. Although it is still early evening Walt is in bed, not lounging in his clothes outside the coverlet, but undressed and laid flat. As he rouses from an uneasy doze, the faithful Horace springs to the bedside.

"I'm right here, Walt. Never mind the bell."

"Horace? Is that you, Horace?"

"Yes. I thought you were reaching up for the bell."

"I was afraid it would fall on me."

"Afraid the bell would fall on you?"

"Not the bell. The pad. I thought there was a great big writing-pad directly over me, and it was going to fall on me and smother me."

"You were dreaming."

"But what a queer dream! I often have it in these days, and wake up trying to keep the writing-pad off with my hands. Yet my writing-pad was always my best friend."

[323]

"Isn't it still? I've copied that letter you gave me, the letter to your friends. You wrote that only five days ago. And here on the table is one for your sister in Vermont."

"Aye, poor Han! Will you address that envelope for me, Horace? And put in the bill that is lying beside the letter. Five dollars. That's right."

"Since you had that attack of pneumonia in December, I've addressed five or six letters for you to your sister Han. And you never forget to enclose a small sum of money."

"My poor Han! The unhappiest of us all! While I can draw half a breath I mustn't forget her."

"There! That's ready to go."

"Han's letter was yesterday's session with the writing-pad. Today's is still under my pillow. Here, take it. Let's hear how it reads."

"What is this? It looks like an advertisement."

"It is. An ad for the New York *Tribune*."

"For a man as sick as you have been, Walt, it's an achievement to write this."

"Maybe, maybe. Let's hear it."

"You shall hear it. 'Walt Whitman wishes respectfully to notify the public that the book "Leaves of Grass," which he has been working on at great intervals and partially issued for the past thirty-five or forty years, is now complete, so to call it—' "

"As complete as it ever will be. Go on."

"—and he would like this new 1892 edition to absolutely supersede all previous ones. Faulty as it is, he decides it as by far his special and entire self-chosen poetical utterance.' "

"That seems all right, Horace?"

"It is more than all right. It sounds the note of victory: the book complete at last."

"It is to go to the *Tribune,* remember."

"I shall see that it reaches them. Speaking of newspapers reminds me. The New York *Telegram* has raised a fund to buy flowers for you. Even at February prices, it would buy more flowers than you could pack into this room. So Tom Harned and Tom Donaldson and I thought we might take part of the money to buy you a new bed."

"What do I want of a new bed? This old one serves me well."

"You need the new bed less on your own account than on Warren Fritzinger's. When he tries to take care of you he finds it hard."

"Aye, he loses me in this bed, I have shrunk so. Warry is a good boy. He's Mary Davis' boy, and as good to me as Mary always has been. Get anything that will make it easier for Warry."

"Of course you can go back to your old bed if you like, when you feel more like your old self."

"I never expect to feel like my old self. I seem to be washed out—to go forth with the tide—the never-returning tide."

"Shall I copy the advertisement to go with your letter to your friends?"

"Yes. Send it to Bucke, Kennedy, Symonds, and John Burroughs."

"I have the list. The original is to go to Maurice Bucke?"

"Yes. Read the letter too, Horace."

"It is dated February sixth, 1892, five days ago. It says, 'Well I must send you all dear fellows a word from my own hand, propp'd up in bed, deadly weak yet, but the spark seems to glimmer—' "

" 'Glimmer,' that's right. Go on."

" 'The doctors and nurses and New York friends as faithful as ever. Here is the advertisement of the '92 edition.' Walt, I can't get over your having written that advertisement."

"Ah, you didn't know the old man had it in him, did you?"

"You will fool us yet."

"Go on. Go on with the letter."

" 'Colonel Ingersoll has been here—sent a basket of champagne.' "

"That was like the dear Colonel. All the good things of earth surround him—and the best of them human kindness."

" 'All are good. Physical condition not so bad as you might suppose, only my sufferings much of the time are fearful. Again I repeat my thanks to you and cheery British friends. Maybe for the last time. My right arm is giving out. Walt Whitman.' "

"You see the arm was strong enough to go on the next day. What did I say the next day, Horace?"

" 'February seventh. Same condition continued. More and more it comes to the fore that the only theory worthy our modern times for great literature, politics and sociology must combine all the best people of all lands, the women not forgetting.—But the mustard plaster on my side is stinging and I must stop. Goodbye to all. W. W.' "

"That mustard plaster is a touch of the actual, the immediate."

"Do you wish me to leave it out of the letter, Walt?
The plaster was off four days ago."

"Let it stand. It completes the picture. You know,
Horace, I've always wanted the complete picture."

"Anything else to add, Walt?"

"Give them all—Bucke, Kennedy, Symonds, all of
them—my undying love."

"Your love is actually undying. Walt, dear Walt,
you do not realize what you have been to us."

"Nor you, perhaps, what you have been to me."

LI

1892

WILLIAMS, HARNED, BRINTON, BUCKE,
BURROUGHS, INGERSOLL, all the dear
companions of Walt's last days.

*In Harleigh Cemetery, Camden, on
a mild March day, the first bluebirds
are singing in the tree-tops. A crowd
numbering thousands is grouped
about a tent with all the sides lifted.
Under this shelter is Walt Whitman's
coffin, surmounted by an ivy wreath,
surrounded by the friends who have
come to speak the last farewell. Tom
Harned, Maurice Bucke and Daniel
Brinton all speak. Only John Burroughs sits apart and is silent.*

*Between the speeches, Francis
Howard Williams reads selected sentences from Confucius, Buddha,
Jesus, the Koran, the Zend Avesta,
and Plato. But he reads all the
twenty-eight lines of the "Death
Song" from "When Lilacs Last."*

" 'Come, lovely and soothing Death,
Undulate round the world, serenely arriving, arriving,

[329]

In the day, in the night, to all, to each,
Sooner or later, delicate Death.

" 'Praised be the fathomless universe,
    For life and joy, and for objects and knowledge curious,
    And for love, sweet love—but praise! praise! praise!
    For the sure-enwinding arms of cool-enfolding Death.

" 'Dark Mother, always gliding near, with soft feet,
    Have none chanted for thee a chant of fullest welcome?
    Then I chant it for thee—I glorify thee above all;
    I bring thee a song that when thou must indeed come, come
        unfalteringly.' "

*Last of all, Colonel Robert Inger-
soll speaks of the dead friend who believed where Ingersoll was brave
enough only to doubt.*

"Greater than all is the true man, and he walked
among his fellow men as such.

"Today we give him back to Mother Nature, to her
clasp and kiss, one of the bravest, sweetest souls that
ever lived in human clay. Charitable as the air and
generous as Nature, he was negligent of all except to
do and say what he believed he should do and should
say.

"And I today thank him, not only for you but for
myself, for all the brave words he has uttered. I thank
him for all the great and splendid words he has said in
favor of liberty, in favor of man and woman, in favor
of motherhood, in favor of fathers, in favor of children, and I thank him for the brave words that he has
said of death.

WALT

"He has lived, he has died, and death is less terrible than it was before. When our turn comes, we will walk down into the 'dark valley of the shadow' holding Walt Whitman by the hand. Long after we are dead, the brave words he has spoken will sound like trumpets to the dying.

"And so I lay this little wreath upon this great man's tomb. I loved him living, and I love him still."

THE END